THE HOUSE TRAP

Barbara Thomason

The HOUSE TRAP

UNITED WRITERS
Cornwall

UNITED WRITERS PUBLICATIONS LTD
Ailsa, Castle Gate, Penzance, Cornwall.
www.unitedwriters.co.uk

British Library Cataloguing in Publication Data:
A catalogue record for this book is
available from the British Library.

ISBN 9781852001995

Printed and bound in Great Britain by
United Writers Publications Ltd.,
Cornwall.

To my daughter
Jan
1953–1994.

Prologue

I gazed silently down at my daughter's grave. From the tree above, a large golden leaf swayed lazily to and fro in the still, cold air. It whispered softly past my cheek until finally coming gently to rest on the hard ground. As I continued to gaze at the headstone I was aware of a quiet, almost dreamlike, state of mind creeping over my chaotic thoughts, the difficult journey to the cemetery almost forgotten. My husband, sensing my mood, waited patiently a few steps behind. Time passed. I remained motionless, incapable of thought or feeling. I wanted to stay deep within this sense of timeless tranquillity. The seconds ticked slowly by, one by one, on and on until a slight breeze rustled through the carpet of leaves on which I was standing. The gentle sound broke into my reverie and I returned to my senses.

My daughter died in a hospice many years ago, and each anniversary would find me at the graveside clutching the obligatory bunch of flowers and staring blankly at the headstone. But this year was different. My husband and I were also to visit my youngest daughter Lucy.

A short walk from the cemetery brought us to Tearo House, which was were my daughter, husband, son and his own young daughter were now living. Loving greetings were exchanged, accompanied by the excited barking from Lucy's four dogs. It was not until we were settled at the wooden kitchen table with warming mugs of coffee, and while we chatted quietly together, that my thoughts began to wander. What could have caused that strange feeling at the cemetery? I pondered, as my gaze roamed around the so familiar room. It was in this house that I had spent the greater part of my life, and although there were small changes it was still the house that I had known from very young childhood. Suddenly I was overwhelmed by a huge wave of emotions and memories. So many voices; laughter and tears, hopes and fears. Tearo House had been my sanctuary and my prison. I had loved and hated him for so many reasons but could not imagine life without him.

Tearo House was built at the end of the twentieth century in a quiet suburb of a small market town in the North of England. It was a typical four-bedroomed Victorian semi-detached property with large gardens back and front. A small drive led to a wooden garage which would adequately house a large car.

There had been two owners. The builder himself lived there for many years, until selling it to the formidable Mrs Bell. It was during her ownership that many changes took place.

Quite what this stern faced woman was hoping to achieve we will never know. What she did was to change a pleasant family home, which was large enough to accommodate a live-in housekeeper, into a building that lost its identity. It was cold, draughty and awkward, and only just tolerable as a family home.

I was a chubby three-year-old in 1937, when I first came to 23 Grange Road with my parents and two brothers. My father was an engineering draughtsman and had been sent by his company in London to their northern branch. Father was to spend a full year there and, as he was missing his family, under his own volition he took out a year's rental on Tearo House. After two weeks, and a long tiring journey, we duly arrived, and I can only imagine Mother's horror when entering her new home. Fortunately she loved her husband and told herself it was only for a year. After all, the gardens were rather lovely.

My parents came from comfortable upper middle class backgrounds. My maternal grandfather was the co-owner and Arts Editor of the *Sunday Times*. Brodie Fraser by name. Mother was the eldest of six siblings and lived in a large house on Wandsworth Common. Mother and her sister were inseparable and their love for each other was almost a tangible force. Artists, poets and aspiring authors were regular visitors to their home and the teenage girls lived life to the full. House parties, tennis parties, dancing at the Savoy and always the theatre. This was the norm as they danced their way through the 1920s.

My paternal grandfather was something to do with shipping and salvage and worked in the City. My father was the eldest of four siblings and at the age of eighteen he joined the London and Scottish Regiment. He was duly sent to France and incredibly survived three long years in the hell of trench warfare. Ironically, he was severely wounded not long before he was due to be demobilised. Although his injuries were severe he survived, but at the tender age of twenty-one he was a broken man. My parents met when Mother was eighteen and Father twenty-one. Their respective parents insisted on a long engagement, and ten years passed before they married.

So there we were. In a cold house. In the cold north east of England. And with a decidedly cool welcome from the neighbours. James was to attend the local grammar school but after a while things were not going too well. His softly spoken BBC accent and courteous behaviour did nothing to endear him to his more rumbustious class mates. Also Father, at his work, and Mother, with the local people, were aware of a slight hostility toward them. In order to lighten our spirits we had a short break at home. It was good to be with our own people; diverse and cosmopolitan – all were welcome. So different to the tensions of the north.

Not long after our return, Mother's sister, Beth, was to visit us. Elizabeth Brodie-Fraser was a woman before her time. Self-assured and fiercely independent, she strode through life in immaculately tailored trousers and silk shirts. Hair the colour of burnished copper, large brown eyes, and a deep husky voice that commanded attention and respect. Stockdale was not ready for a woman such as Beth.

Tearo House came alive with the arrival of this lively young woman. Her chatter and laughter filled the bare rooms as we played hilarious games of hide and seek. Her cheerful disposition and positive outlook on life was exactly the tonic we needed and the year would soon pass.

Surprisingly, the days seemed to progress steadily by, and the time for us to return home was drawing closer. A quiet air of excitement was growing between my parents and we began arrangements for our return. Mother armed herself with buckets and mops, and slowly began to work her way through the shabby rooms. Father happily tidied the garden, and James could hardly contain his excitement at the thought of seeing his friends again.

Two weeks before we were due to leave Stockdale, completely without warning, that nebulous, mercurial force called fate crashed into our lives with news for Father that was to completely change the course of my life.

Father was a rather shy, studious man and the quality of his work had attracted the attention of a rival company. They offered him a better paid position, but it meant that he would have to stay in Stockdale for a longer period. Father nearly cracked under the strain and my parents talked long into the night before a decision was made. Eventually an agreement was made between the company and the disagreeable Mrs Bell that we would remain in Stockdale for the next three years.

It took Mother and, in particular, James many weeks to accept Father's decision, and knowing that Mrs Bell had been decidedly reluctant to renew the rental agreement did nothing to alleviate the dreadful home sickness we were all experiencing. A bitter winter followed, and the relief of surviving the north-east snow and winds was short lived at the realisation that we would have to go through it all again. But with the spring came news that Granny, Mother's mother, was to make the long journey north. The day of her arrival came and Mother and I knew from experience that Granny knew full well how to make a grand entrance.

She did not disappoint. Tall, straight, flashing dark eyes under thick white hair and an astonishing hat, her elegant gloved hand holding a silver topped ebony cane, she emerged gracefully from the taxi. We knew that curtains would be twitching. Eventually, after unpacking, a hot meal and settling in the shabby armchair in the warmest corner of the house, came the moment I had been waiting for. From her voluminous handbag she produced the familiar slim red box of Balkan Sobranie. The glowing jewel-like colours and musky aroma of these little Russian cigarettes are my one abiding memory of Granny. Before marriage she had been the headmistress of a gentile girl's school in Aberdeen and had never lost her air of authority and musical, lilting Aberdonian accent.

Her time with us did not bring the joyful laughter that Beth's presence would inspire, but Granny patiently answered all the questions that puzzled my four-year-old mind.

Granny did not linger long in the uncomfortable house for she was of an age that could not easily cope with a lumpy mattress. Her departure was slightly more subdued than her arrival, apart from some confusion concerning her treasured hat box. Eventually Father was able to settle her comfortably on the train to King's Cross, along with a large tip to the kindly guard. A late spring brought life-giving gentle sun and the house began to relax. Gone were the creaks and groans caused by the bitter north-east winds, and as the large rooms grew warmer in the soft air they seemed to smile at our quiet pleasure.

Once again, fate tipped her toes into our lives in the shape of Uncle John.

He was Father's younger brother and by sheer coincidence had accepted the position of Senior Chemist at a large chemical company situated on the outskirts of Stockdale. He wrote to ask whether he could stay with us until finding other lodgings. Of course, we were thrilled to have a relative of our own living with us and he duly arrived driving his car.

Owning a car put us on a different level to our neighbours and once again the so called 'goings-on' at No. 23 added extra spice to the local gossip.

My mischievous golden haired, blue-eyed mother obviously enjoyed the notoriety she was attracting. Telling me much later on that people wondered which man she was married to and just who was the red haired beauty who kept appearing.

"Can you believe it, darling?" Mother would giggle. "These people are so naïve!"

Meanwhile, with the unexpected bonus of Uncle John's car, we discovered that we were living on the boundary of one of the most beautiful parts of the country. The savage beauty of the North York Moors was practically on our doorstep. Mother was captivated by the tumbling waterfalls and boundless heather-clad moors under endless skies, and seemed to recapture her joy of life once more. The craggy coastline, with smuggler haunted cottages that tumbled down the cliff side, intrigued Father and Uncle John, whilst the rock pools and soft sandy beaches gave endless pleasure to my brothers and myself.

The summer of 1938 seemed to disappear in a haze of busy

days in the garden and life renewing picnics on the moors. We were soon approaching another year.

Comforted by a happier Christmas, I even had a pillowcase full of goodies; the first and last time, I fear. We began to talk tentatively about our return home.

Somehow, Mother survived another winter coping with the scullery and the summer would bring another holiday in the south. Time was passing quite nicely. Summer finally arrived, bringing wildflower meadows beyond the garden, and the tree house in the ancient old willow that James was constructing began to take shape. Strangely, the long summer days brought a quiet contentment within our little family. Slowly but steadily the longed for day on which we could finally leave Stockdale was almost in sight.

But this was September 1939, and as my parents listened in horror to those doom-laden words 'that Britain was at war with Germany' we knew we were hopelessly trapped.

Chapter One

To a five-year-old child the words 'there is a war on' held little meaning, but I was fully aware of the controlled underlying fear in my parent's quiet voices, and my father's face, when in repose, had the look of a man haunted by unspeakable memories.

It took my parents many weeks to accept the inevitability of their situation. They both needed the support of their families but had to acknowledge that Stockdale, although surrounded by vital steel and dock yards, was a safer place than London. Inexplicably the role that Tearo House played in their lives had become reversed and was now their sanctuary. Sadly, my mother never could and never did feel any affection for the old place. Her longing for the close proximity to theatres, galleries and museums, the cosmopolitan attitude and warmer climate was almost unbearable at times.

Uncle John had unexpectedly departed in a flurry of confetti and congratulations, after a whirlwind romance with a local girl, and gone to pastures new. He was dreadfully missed, along with our life-enhancing picnics in the glorious countryside. But I, in particular, missed his gentle hugs and cuddles, all of which a little girl might have expected from her father. However, I instinctively knew these were not forthcoming from my particular parent.

Stockdale was preparing for war. All wrought iron railings from parks, schools and cemeteries had been removed as they were needed to be melted down and reused as ammunition.

Church bells were to be rung only in the event of an invasion and fear was growing within people sensing their lives were to change forever. This ancient little market town seemed to be holding its breath against an unknown future.

13

Being five years old in 1939, I was due to start school in September. This was delayed for three weeks as the state of war had thrown the country into chaos. Eventually, I made my entry into school, but everything in my young life was changing and I felt unsure about the future.

Chapter Two

Grange Road was tree-lined, with houses set back in well kept gardens. The residents were either retired or professional people, with only two other families having children. At one end a family run business of bakery and shop kept the locals supplied with their mouth-watering freshly baked bread. At the other end stood the church beyond which Grange Farm spread its many acres. Halfway along Grange Road a bright red telephone kiosk, complete with its yellow directory, stood next to the Institute. This large hall played an important part in the lives of the local community and became for me my first experience of school.

A quarter of a mile away was the large Victorian school to which I should eventually attend. However, the infant section was being hastily prepared as a field hospital and, before the transition was completed, I, along with my new class mates, began our school days in the Institute.

My first year of schooling was spent sitting on the hard wooden floors of the Institute and eventually of the large school hall. I had been dreading this day, as I knew that James had had trouble with his school. I wondered if I would suffer the misery that he had so obviously experienced. James did his loving best to reassure me: "Don't worry, Mabs," he told me, "you will make friends with other little girls, which will be much better than messing about with Mark and me," but his voice did not carry the conviction of his words. However, in the event, I was thankfully blessed with a wonderful infant teacher.

Unfortunately, her influence did not reach beyond my first year and I had to cope with my tears alone. My name was Martha Ferguson, known as Mabs to my family, and along with my southern accent I was the object of much teasing and laughter. But armed with wise advice from James, I learnt how to handle the situation and slowly made one or two friends.

Meanwhile, the Second World War was taking hold, and rumours of invasion by Germany were looking increasingly possible.

We small children had to be taught about the dangers that lay ahead. A large air raid shelter was speedily erected at the bottom of the school yard rather too close to a small beck. The proximity of running water meant that the shelter was extremely damp. Small pools of water collected on the floor and the walls were clammy to the touch. We entered by a trap door and, climbing down a rusting iron ladder, and aided only by a hand-held torch held by our teacher, we were ordered to sit quietly on damp wooden benches. A second drill practice found me clinging to the ladder and sobbing with tears of terror at the cold, damp darkness below.

I resolved there and then that I would rather face Hitler and the entire German army than ever use that shelter again.

Chapter Three

It was the summer of 1940 and Father was looking weary, his tired eyes showing the strain of long forgotten memories returning.

Food, clothing, coal and petrol – all were now rationed. Rumours of the evacuation of our army from the beaches of Dunkirk shocked my parents to such an extent that even they began to fear invasion of our small island was possible.

Since coming to Stockdale, Mother's longing for live theatre was only partially satisfied by visiting the local cinema. Every week she and I would thrill to the silver screen. Not only were we entertained but we saw at first hand the progress of the Second World War by courtesy of Pathé News. Mother felt that I was old enough to try to understand something of what was happening in the world. So, along with my bedtime fairy stories, I had rather more disturbing things of which to dream.

Rumours of unspeakable atrocities taking place in countries that had been occupied were being whispered through the town and mother was worried. After much thought and heartfelt prayer my gentle, all loving, mother came up with a plan. One evening, after a frugal supper, Father was relocated to kitchen duties while she gathered us around the table. We all looked at her expectantly, wondering what was wrong, why was she so serious? I panicked. Was she ill? Please God, not that!

The silence grew. We began to fidget. She looked round the table again, from James to myself and Mark, then in a quiet controlled voice spoke. "As you all know we are at war and there is a distinct possibility that we will be invaded by Germany. Now I cannot and will not let this happen to my children," she paused. We waited expectantly, then she continued in a voice devoid of any emotion: "It is completely unthinkable that you should fall into German hands, so I will find a gun, shoot each one of you very quickly, then kill myself."

There was a stunned silence as we looked at her in complete horror. I opened my mouth, but there was no sound. I was frozen to my chair. I could see Mother's hands shaking as they lay in her lap and I knew she meant every word.

Four-year-old Mark, thinking it was a joke, was the first to speak.

"Are you really going to shoot us Mummy? Gosh, what fun, but you won't really hurt us will you?" his voice trailed away uncertainly.

I continued to stare at her, still incapable of speech, then eleven-year-old James burst out, his voice cracking with emotion, "Don't be so stupid, Mother, you can't do a thing like that. And anyway, where would you find a gun? It's a ridiculous idea," he finished scathingly.

Another silence, and when she spoke her eyes were cold with anger: "Oh, my darlings, if this country is invaded, I promise you I will do this terrible thing."

Looking back, I was never quite sure where Father stood in all this scheming, but I am absolutely certain she meant every word. Certain thoughts and actions that in peacetime would be considered abnormal were quite acceptable in times of war, and Mother was not alone in her wild plan.

Chapter Four

Before this murderous event could take place, Mother had to cope with the fortnightly delivery of coal. This event, in itself, is of little or no interest to the reader, so in order to explain I must first describe the kitchen and scullery at Tearo House. It is in this area that Mrs Bell's attempts at home improvements had gone slightly awry.

To enter the kitchen I had known as a child, a steep flight of stairs led from the hall into a small stone paved area which held three doors. One to the cupboard under the stairs, another to a smaller cupboard, and the third opened into what had originally been a square kitchen with a large pantry. This had been removed, making a longer room, but in doing so it had lost its Victorian proportions and elegance. The original kitchen range which heated the water and on which the cooking was done, had been replaced by an open coal fire with back boiler. On the south facing wall there was a sash window and a heavy wooden door that opened directly into the garden. In the alcove to the right of the fireplace, the thick wall had been partially removed to enter a new addition to this living area.

To describe this room as a scullery would be a slight misnomer as it gave only the minimum protection against the elements. Two walls and the roof were made of corrugated iron, the others were brick. In the left corner there was a cubicle that had once housed the outside lavatory and was now our coal bunker. One day, when Mother entered this place for a shovel of coal, a huge rat, teeth barred, hurled itself at her lap. It slithered down her skirt and disappeared, we knew not where. Understandably, Mother was so shaken by this incident that Father invested in a farm cat. "It's a bloody good ratter, Mr F," Father was assured by old Mr Robinson. Father did his utmost to improve this primitive room for Mother, and his DIY skills were most impressive.

He made a high standing wooden meat safe, freshly painted in white, and a strong draining board attached to the stone Belfast sink. The meat safe was lined in metal, and underneath was a small table where the pans and kitchen utensils were kept. Next appeared a shiny new roller towel holder from which Mother would hang a brightly coloured towel; the only splash of colour in this grey room. A small iron-framed gas cooler, a wooden-topped table wringer and a zinc wash tub completed Mother's state of the art scullery.

Every fortnight, Mr Watson, aided by his two strong but silent sons, would deliver our coal ration. Whenever I could I would wait with Mother and observe this little ritual, knowing what was to come. The men's heavy boots would clatter through the long front garden, past the garage and down the side of the house until growing silent on the muddy path by the side of the scullery. The heavy sacks of coal held securely on their bent shoulders almost filled the little doorway, then they moved across the room and into the cubicle. With a thunderous roar two sacks of black gold were emptied into our kitchen. Billowing clouds of acrid smelling coal dust followed, to eventually settle on every surface and into every corner, and with a sinking heart I knew this meant hours of cleaning to make the scullery habitable again. When the delivery was completed and Mr Watson had been paid, I would listen quietly while they 'put the world to rights'.

Chapter Five

It was a hot day in late august 1940 and my sixth birthday had passed. Tearo House was visibly relaxing. Like a sleeping cat slowly stretching only to doze again in the warm air. Doors and windows were open and bright sunlight flooded through the large windows breathing fresh life into the shabby rooms. The garden and fields beyond were at their best, and the heavy heat had rejuvenated the house fly population to such an extent that the fly papers hanging from the ceiling light in the kitchen had to be changed twice daily. Children's voices at play could be heard and Mother watched lovingly over her small flock.

Three hundred miles away in those clear blue skies, the Battle of Britain was playing out its dance of death, while the slaughter of our young men continued. It was then that Father finally cracked.

It was Friday evening and Mother was preparing a light evening meal in the sweltering heat of the scullery. Father was due home from work and we waited to hear his footsteps on the garden path. As usual, Mother came to greet him, her face rather pink with the heat. He hesitated in the open doorway and then the angry words poured out in a rush.

"Well, that's it, Lassie. I have finally done it. I am not taking it any more. I have been pushed around all my life by petty-minded little pen-pushing, arse licking bloody minded bureaucrats. So I have told them to keep their job and I have resigned."

There was a long silence and the colour drained slowly from Mother's face.

"You have done what?" she practically spat out the words. "You have done what?" she repeated in shocked disbelief.

The reality of the enormity of the meaning of his words began to sink into her brain!

"Oh, Alec, how could you? How could you? How on earth am I to manage? How could you?" By now her voice was shaking and she was near to tears.

"That's alright, Harriet, you will manage somehow. You always do and I will get another job,' came the reply, and with that he turned and left the room.

On that sultry summer's day, Tearo House smiled quietly to himself. He had found his first victim.

Father's controlled resentment at mindless authoritarianism was born from the mud and carnage of the trenches during the First World War. Unknown to Mother, he had been under pressure to join the Draughtsman's Union. This had never been an issue in the London office in which he had previously worked, so when the final ultimatum came from a particularly obnoxious militant member, he snapped.

After Father's dramatic resignation my parents talked for many hours. Mother's anger subsided and they seemed relatively content together. But when I snuggled up to Mother in my usual place in church, I sensed her prayers were more a cry of utter despair instead of the normal comfort she received.

Chapter Six

Winter was coming and there was a chill in the air.

Naked trees displayed their empty branches against leaden skies and the locals sensed snow before Christmas.

Father was now officially drawing dole money which lasted for two weeks only. Beyond that there was nothing more to come. The outlook was bleak indeed.

Three weeks later we were in trouble. Amazingly Father had found another position, but after bills had been paid we were left without money for food.

The feeling of shame at Father's unemployment was growing between James and myself, but Father, James and Mark would never know of the shame that I felt at Mother's secret. Mother had to take me into her confidence as there was only one solution to our predicament. We had to resort to the lifesaver of the very poor, which was a visit to a pawnbroker.

Mother's treasured and highly valuable engagement ring was to be the sacrifice. So, one gloomy afternoon, Mother and I walked out of Grange Road and turned left. With the cemetery on the right, then muddy waste ground on our left, we passed under a foul smelling tunnel and into another world.

Row upon row of narrow streets with back to back houses were to be seen, with barefoot urchins playing in the gutter and hungry stray dogs snapping at our heels. Our hands tightly clasped and hearts beating, we stared in disbelief at the three huge brass balls hanging above the pawnbroker's doorway.

With one last nervous glance over her shoulder, Mother pushed open the heavy door! A brass bell jangled noisily on its spring and we both jumped at the shrill clanking.

A soft hissing sound greeted us and I looked up to see a large heavy-duty oil lamp hanging from the ceiling. The room was dark and gloomy, and the heavy shadows made it difficult to make out a large man in brown overalls standing behind a solid wooden counter. Bare floorboards creaked beneath our feet and a sour musty smell caught the back of my throat.

Mother was tearful with shame and desperation as she greeted Mr Bird with a quiet, "Good evening."

On hearing her voice, Mr Bird's rather wary attitude softened. When she hesitantly explained that this was her first time in such an establishment, his rough voice became gentle in his explanation of the terms and conditions of the transaction.

The precious ring was duly handed over and money was exchanged. With a tearful smile Mother bid Mr Bird farewell and, as the door closed behind us, she cried, "Oh, Mabs, let's get out of this dreadful place!"

With clasped hands, we almost ran back to the familiarity and safety of Tearo House.

The redemption of the ring was paid for by Beth, who was horrified to hear that our situation had become so desperate that this shameful act had been the only answer.

Chapter Seven

I had a friend; Penelope Frobisher by name. She had everything I did not; toys, pretty frocks and shoes. She even had a real leather peggy purse while I had to carry my handkerchief in the pocket of my navy blue knickers. Naturally, I found this particularly demeaning to my six-year-old dignity. She also had rather beautiful blonde softly waving hair, whereas mine was short, straight and mousy. How could I not hate her? In spite of this, we played together relatively contentedly, with only occasional spats of feminine bitchiness.

Amongst her box of goodies, Penny had a beautiful doll. The most beautiful doll I had ever seen. Dressed in Dutch national costume, she wore painted clogs, a pristine white apron and a divine little pointed white cap. This covered her long yellow plaits which could be undone and re-dressed in some other style. A littler girl's dream doll. When we were together, Penny would let me play with this magnificent doll and I began to long for one of my own. I longed for this doll with such an overwhelming passion that I can recall the feelings even now.

Christmas was approaching and, armed only with her meagre budget, Mother began her search for my doll. A week before Christmas, Penelope won first prize for the Best Milk Top Pompom competition at school. I came third.

Magnanimous in her success, Penelope allowed me to have 'Gretchen' the doll at my home for a few days. I was overwhelmed by her generosity as I held the large doll in my arms.

b

Chapter Eight

It was Christmas Eve and there was one last purchase to be made to complete the preparations for the big day. Helped by Mother's advice, my brothers and I were to spend our precious sweet coupons. As the allowance for the month was only eight ounces, with two ounces extra for children at Christmas, it was imperative we made the right decision. Father had been left at home on postal duties, as Mother was anxiously waiting for the hamper from Fortnum and Mason to arrive. This generous gift was a birthday present to Mother from her brother and was pivotal to our festivities. Uncle Don was a professional soldier and, after a long and distinguished career, retired as Lieutenant Colonel Fraser. Happily, the Fraser siblings had a close relationship all their lives and were justly proud of their younger brother.

Eventually, the expected knock came at the front door and Mother and I raced upstairs to receive the parcel. After all the mouthwatering contents had been duly inspected and stored away, Mother made our evening cup of cocoa. With the firelight flickering on our handmade coloured paper chains, and the well worn Christmas tree in its usual place on the kitchen table, we all fell silent to dream about the day to come.

By six o'clock on Christmas Day morning, Mark and I, happily ignoring the thick layer of ice on our bedroom window, had eaten our entire month's ration of sweets. James, who had a will of iron, was sucking contentedly on a large toffee, knowing that his choice of sweets would last the month at a rate of one a day. On hearing the laughter, Mother joined us. Huddled in her thin dressing gown she saw me holding the parcel that was the doll.

Her eyes were shining with excitement as she waited for me to unwrap the parcel. "I do hope you like it, darling." She smiled lovingly at me, trying to hold back her happy expectation of my excited gratitude.

But something was wrong, terribly wrong. This did not feel like chubby, solid Gretchen. This parcel was too small and soft and light to the touch. My hands trembled as I tore away the paper and string. There was a silence, as the boys, knowing of my hopes, nervously waited for my reaction. The last pieces of paper fell away to reveal a beautifully handmade doll in Russian national costume. From her knee-length leather boots to the embroidered headscarf that covered two thick plaits of dark hair, the doll was a work of art.

Choking back my complete and utter disappointment, I whispered a tearful, "Thank you, Mummy, she is lovely."

Completely misunderstanding my tears, she held me in her arms. "I am so very glad you like her, darling, that's all that matters," she whispered with relief.

Mother told me much later on that Mrs Price, a new neighbour, was a professional doll maker and, unknown to Father, Mother had been making weekly instalments to pay for this expensive doll. Happily, with time and a lot of thought, I came to love the doll and appreciate its true value.

Chapter Nine

As my eighth birthday passed, I was beginning to feel bewildered and shamed by Father's cavalier attitude towards his employment. I also hated my visits to the pawnbroker with Mother, as I knew that she too felt such shame at our position. It was a long time before I realised how his time in France had so deeply affected this young and sensitive man.

When my parents came to Stockdale, the social life they had known in London came to an abrupt end, so Mother instinctively turned to the church from where she had always received comfort, support and friendship. Sadly, we were met with only a polite acknowledgement of our presence.

Father was not a churchgoer. After his week's work was completed he was content to bury himself in his beloved books, or work out his frustration on an intricate piece of carpentry, at which he excelled.

In spite of regular attendance in church with Mother and Mark, no attempt at genuine friendship was forthcoming. Even though, as teenagers I sang in the choir and Mark joined the badminton club, and we both took part in Scottish dancing, it was all to no avail.

I often wondered whether it was the shabbiness of our living quarters in Tearo House that caused the breach between ourselves and our neighbours, but I held my head high as I knew that our lives had not always been so impoverished. Within Tearo House there were many signs of a past discreet wealth, in the shapes of an exquisite Dresden China figurine, or the napkin rings made of delicate silver work with our initials embossed on a raised medallion. There was the quirky Clarice Cliff tea set and a complete canteen of solid silver cutlery from soup to fish. But I particularly loved the evocative paintings of the interior of Westminster Abbey. They were painted by an aunt of Father's and she had had her work shown in the Royal Academy of Art. They were thoughtful and mysterious and I often caught Mother gazing wistfully at them, so obviously longing to be back in her beloved London.

When writing of these small happenings in my life, I am beginning to realise quite how unhappy Mother was while living in the north. She was an instinctive homemaker to us all; loving, supportive and completely reliable, but beneath this motherly persona lay a restless, enquiring spirit, craving the excitement and stimulation of life in the London. I knew that Father was as unhappy as she but was now unable to alter their situation.

Their happiness and love for each other since coming to Stockdale was obvious, as shown by old photographs, but tragically her beloved Father's death coincided with Father's career change, thereby tying them more firmly to the north. The onset of yet another war in their still young lives was the final straw and it seemed as if that impossible, unfathomable, mysterious house had caught us in his web.

Chapter Ten

Time passed. Another Christmas arrived and was soon over, but the contents of the hamper this year were greatly reduced. Battles were being fought overseas and our ships were being sunk at sea. News of the sinking of the *Jervis Bay* filtered through and Father was deeply saddened by the report. He had served for many years as a ship's engineer during his ten year engagement to Mother.

Bombing of our cities and towns continued and there were times when news from Beth was extremely worrying. One dark night, when Mother was about to settle a still sleepy Mark and myself in our neighbour's air raid shelter, she heard the heart-stopping whistle of a falling bomb. As she was still at the entrance of the shelter, she screamed for Father, and she practically threw herself down into the earth-smelling darkness. Father was too late and the blast threw him bodily against a thick hawthorn hedge. The blast rendered him unconscious momentarily and he was severely bruised and cut from the hedge, but otherwise nothing too serious. The bomb was the second of three dropped that night by a pilot on his way home to Germany. The first fell in a field behind the church, the second fell on two homes only five houses from Tearo House, and the third further down the field behind us, luckily avoiding more homes. The tragic deaths of our neighbours left an air of deep despondency amongst the residents of Grange Road for quite some time.

Father had persevered with his horticultural efforts and had had some success with his vegetables. This was just as well, as his rapport with the earth did not extend to his employers, and once again he resigned. Tearo House quietly watched Father. There was the usual cool atmosphere between my parents until he found other employment, which fortunately he always did as the alternative was unthinkable.

There were more visits to the pawnshop for Mother and I, where now we were on chatting terms with Mr Bird. The redemption of Mother's precious ring had to be timed with the rebate from the gas meter when emptied. Sadly this was not always possible, as Father's irrational periods of employment were never at regular intervals. Mother was aware that he was becoming more aggressive with his employers, stubbornly arguing his point until it led to dismissal. His irresponsible actions then led to Mother having to make impossible choices, one of which left me with a rather unhappy memory.

It was inevitable that the choice between rental money or food would arise, and so the day arrived when Mrs Bell and her big black bag came knocking on the back door. Mother and I clung together on the other side, hardly daring to breath.

"Mrs Ferguson, I am here to collect my rental money. Are you there, Mrs Ferguson?" Another loud knock at the door. "Mrs Ferguson, I know you are there. Open this door at once!" Her voice grew louder as she rattled the handle. "I know you are there, Mrs Ferguson. Open this door at once! Do you hear me?"

By now she was banging at the door in such anger that it was shaking behind us, as we clung together shaking with guilt and fear. Mother's eyes were closed in silent prayer and I began to whimper.

"Mrs Ferguson, if you do not pay up next week I will have you out of here. Do you hear me?" There was another furious rattle at the handle, and as a parting shot, she shouted: "I will have the bailiffs in if you do not pay up next week. Do you understand me, Mrs Ferguson?"

Mother sank into her chair after Mrs Bell left, pale-faced and visibly shaken. I made her a cup of tea and did my best to reassure her, but at that moment I almost hated my Father.

Chapter Eleven

My childhood memories of the Second World War are primarily of hunger, cold and the nagging fear that terrifying things could happen at any moment in time. Also, Father's favourite mantra: "No, you can't have it. There is a war on and we can't afford it."

This was always the reply to my constant angry requests for toys, sweets, shoes and ice cream, and even a pony. I knew that this final plea was pushing my luck a little too far, but always felt that it was worth a try.

During all those summers of the 1940s, my brothers and I played happily in the field beyond the garden, lost in our own little worlds.

On the other side of the beck, in another large field, there was a chicken farm. So, although Grange Road was a suburb of Stockdale, there was a distinctly rural feel to the area.

Another occupant in the field was Mr Robinson's beloved old horse, Betty. We were told to keep away from her as she was a grumpy old girl, but I loved to watch her from a safe distance and imagine riding her bareback in a wild gallop on some exotic beach, with the wind blowing in my hair.

One hot summer's night during an air raid, a low flying aeroplane frightened the animal and she bolted and fell into the deep-sided, fast flowing beck. A frantic Mr Robinson called out Father and four other men, who were also in their garden shelters, and, aided with thick ropes and instructions from the old farmer, they eventually dragged the near drowning horse to safety.

This dangerous rescue took place within a short distance of

falling bombs and heavy gunfire, without any thought for their own safety.

Finally, the cold, wet and exhausted men settled Old Betty safely in her stable while the tearful Mr Robinson tried to express his eternal gratitude.

The next day, Father and his companions were hailed as the local heroes.

In contrast to the warmer weather of the summers, the winter months could at times be almost unbearable. Tearo House would be heard to complain quite audibly by his groans, creaks and moans as the bitter wind blew through the cracks and under the doors, while Jack Frost's icy fingers slithered into all the upstairs rooms. The exposed water pipes in the scullery would burst regularly, turning the stone floor into an ice rink, and Father had to become our own personal plumber. Mother battled wearily with the dreadful condensation that at times would force her to don an old raincoat of Father's in order to protect her clothing from the rusty droplets of water.

The constant stepping up and down between the scullery and kitchen, carrying trays of food and nourishment, were year by year beginning to tire her seemingly inexhaustible energy. The worry of the ever diminishing store of coal, built up during the summer months, only added to the misery of winter.

As the war progressed, food became harder to acquire and our lack of money meant that we had only the basic ration on which to live. This was the absolute minimum for survival, and consequently Mark and I lacked the protein needed by growing children, thereby causing problems in later life. Father's vegetables and fruit helped out, but there were days when, with a sinking heart, I would watch Mother sit quietly in the corner by the fire with only a bowl of thin potato soup, while we had the more nourishing food.

I am strongly convinced that it was only the deep sustaining love between the two sisters that gave Mother the strength to cope with these dreadful years. Beth made only two visits during that period, and on one occasion I went with Mother to meet her at the station. I will never forget how Mother froze on the spot as the tall, elegant white haired figure smilingly approached.

"Oh, Beth, what on earth has happened to your beautiful hair?" she gasped.

From early girlhood Mother had admired her younger sister's vibrant coloured hair and she was deeply saddened at the loss of such beauty.

We listened, unbelievingly, as Beth told how she had had to carry Granny down three flights of burning stairs one night when their flat had caught fire during an air raid.

The relative safety of Tearo House was able to give Beth the long overdue respite she needed from the horrors of war-torn London. For Mother, and also Father, simply to be with her sister was all that she needed to recharge her batteries in order to cope with a family in that awkward old house. As I watched the three adults together, talking, laughing and teasing I could see that they were a complete unit, almost as one.

Chapter Twelve

I have written a great deal about Mother, but she was absolutely pivotal to all our lives. So it is painful to recall that during my teenage years I broke her heart by bringing shame and disgrace to my family. However, I digress, and will return to that later.

I have always longed for a sister but I loved my two brothers dearly. James I quite simply adored, whereas Mark and I were joined at the hip.

James had a restless, enquiring mind and, with the help of two close friends, was constantly involved in one bizarre experiment or the other. However, there were times when the help of an adoring, willing little sister was needed.

Over the years, I was very nearly electrocuted, nearly fell from a badly constructed swing twenty feet in the air, and nearly hurt myself severely in an attempt to gauge the mph of a four-wheeled cart without brakes. In fairness to James, he had dug a large hole in order to stop my flight – in theory, of course!

But my eccentric brother surpassed himself by organising a boxing match between Penny and myself.

One summer afternoon, we found ourselves weighed down with heavy leather boxing gloves in the middle of a makeshift ring, complete with sponges, buckets of water and towels.

From opposite corners, two older brothers were shouting encouragement:

"Go on, Mabs."

"Hit her one, Penny. Hit her back."

"Hit her harder, Mabs."

"Come on, Penny, you must hit her."

Dazed and confused, I closed my eyes and lunged out with my gloved hand. Surprisingly, I hit her on the chin and she fell down and cried.

James proudly declared me to be the winner, while Penny's disgruntled brother accepted defeat.

Quite what it was to prove, only James would ever know.

But it was James who taught me to tell the time. It was James who taught me how to ride Father's old bicycle, and it was James who taught me how to identify enemy aeroplanes.

During the war years we had to make our own fun, as toys were unavailable. Long country walks and hilarious card and board games, where Mother would cheat outrageously, and the all important radio, were our social pastimes, but books were the mainstay of our pleasure and remained so all our lives.

The tree house in the old willow was James's sanctuary. Nobody could reach him there, not even Father.

I spent my childhood desperately trying to invade James's privacy, but to no avail. I was the typical annoying little sister, intent on joining in with her elder brother's manly pursuits, but his love for me lasted to the end.

As children we were undernourished, inadequately dressed and had very few toys. James contracted the killer disease, diphtheria, I had severe bronchitis and asthma and Mark was a little frail. Beth always paid the doctor's bills. I could tell of some heartbreaking episodes when we were cold, hungry and even without footwear for school, but we knew we were loved.

In spite of our poverty, we were relatively happy at Tearo House because of its rural position. Beyond the garden lay a smallholding with several strange animals, and across the beck there was a huge chicken farm. Most of our time was spent in the glorious wildflower meadow. James would prowl along the beck side with his air pistol, shooting the rats that occasionally invaded the garden, while Mark and I would wander around lost in our own little worlds of exploration and discovery.

Within the large garden, we would play cricket with Father, climb trees, build bonfires and pick fruit. Above the house and garden towered the huge old willow tree telling us of the seasons. The sparkling, golden green light, emanating from its slender leaves and catkins, swirled around us all summer. I would lie on my back, gazing up into its mysterious almost ethereal depths, dreaming my dreams. Winter would bring the dark outline of its sturdy, naked branches showing starkly against a winter sky, together with the thick deep snow that invariably fell in the north. We would build large snowmen. Hilarious snow fights would occur when helping Father clear the garden paths.

We were also very aware that a war was being fought, which is why James did his best to teach Mark and myself aircraft recognition, as he feared for our safety.

As I recall the past, I realise that the lack of immediate family, in the shape of grandparents, uncles and aunts, caused us to rely on and support each other in every way without question. Therefore, the love between us held a special dimension not always known in other families.

Chapter Thirteen

1944, and there was no sign that this long and bitter war was coming to any satisfactory conclusion. I was ten years old during the summer and beginning to feel as if my whole life was to be played out in the theatre of war. Memories of our carefree days in London were fading and our lives had to be lived from day to day, never knowing what tomorrow would bring. There was no escaping the trappings of war, it flowed around us imperceptibly in terrifying blackouts and air raids, and eternal queuing for food. It was in the songs that were sung, headlines in newspapers and all young men in uniform.

We even had to recognise the familiar voice of a newsreader in case the radio station was taken over by the enemy. To mark my first decade, Mother had promised that somehow she would organise a party. It would be my first and, in the event, my last.

Some weeks before the great day was due I have a vivid memory of a night in the air raid shelter. It was a warm night in June with a clear bright moon. We were all in our usual positions, James in his bedroom refusing to leave the house and we three settled deep down in the shelter. Father always waited and watched outside by the door.

It began as a distant rumble, slowly growing closer and closer. The heavy beat grew louder and louder until the steady throbbing of hundreds of engines overwhelmed our senses. The very ground was shaking as we watched, transfixed, wave after wave of aeroplanes moving steadily and with a menacing determination over our heads. Their bulbous shapes silhouetted against a brilliant moon whose light perversely portrayed them almost as objects of beauty. After what seemed to be an eternity, for we were numb with shock, Father spoke: "Dear God, some poor blighter is getting it tonight."

Safely back in Tearo House with mugs of cocoa, we could see that Father was visibly shaken, and as Mother tucked us up in bed she too was unusually subdued. We waited anxiously for the news next day and heard that the Normandy Landings had begun.

6th June 1944, D-Day, is recorded as the largest military operation of the Second World War, and Mother's brother was awarded the OBE for his outstanding contribution on the organisation of this battle. The day of my birthday dawned bright and clear. Miraculously, Mother had acquired a proper party frock for the occasion and my excitement was almost unbearable.

My four guests arrived bearing gifts – what joy. There was a picnic of tiny sandwiches and lemonade on a large rug that was spread beneath sun dappled trees offering shade from the hot afternoon sun. Then Mother appeared with the cake. It was a plain sponge made with dried eggs and dried milk, topped with a sugar icing. Not to be outdone by the complete lack of cake decorations, Mother had found the perfect solution. Ten brightly coloured little plastic thimbles to replace the candles, so that each child could take home a colour of their choice as a memento of the day.

The next day the word spread and Mother's ingenuity made a lasting impression on her neighbours. I will never forget that carefree day of sunshine and laughter, and the sheer exhilaration at being just a little girl in a pretty frock frolicking on green lawns with my friends. It marked the beginning of the end of my childhood; a childhood so different to those of today. For I, like so many other children, had had to grow old before their time.

With the advent of the Normandy Landings our terrible six years of war came to a conclusion ending in victory, and on the 8th May 1945 peace was finally declared in Europe. Of course, it would not be until 2nd September and VJ Day before the Second World War ended.

Chapter Fourteen

The cessation of hostilities did not immediately turn the country into a land of milk and honey. Quite the opposite. Our daily lives remained the same, in that strict rationing continued, as did the shortage of all commodities from knicker elastic to petrol.

1947 brought the marriage of Princess Elizabeth and Prince Philip as a much needed morale booster to post-war Britain. Hundreds of romantically minded girls and women sacrificed their precious clothing coupons towards the making of the wedding dress.

By this time, James was well on his way to a successful career as an airline captain, but with his departure the dynamics of our little group changed. It is always difficult for parents to watch their fledglings leave the nest, but for Mother and Father James had been their last immediate link with the south. He had been old enough for them to share many memories of that period and even helped with my recollections of the past. There was an imperceptible change between my parents as Father slowly began to lose grip on reality. I was to learn later that there had been many heated discussions over James's education. Father was adamant that he was earning enough to pay for his son's training college, completely ignoring the practicalities of life.

Father was still employed but was now reduced to hard manual labour. He would laughingly tell of digging ditches with ex-murderers from Durham Gaol and Mother knew his condition was becoming serious. She, too, was reaching breaking point. As always, Beth came to the rescue. Sadly, James was never to know that she had been his benefactor and always believed that Father paid his fees. Obviously Mother and I had kept our secrets about our complete lack of financial support only too well.

I find it difficult to write about this period, but recently I was to see, quite suddenly and very dramatically, a piece of film showing Father in France. One evening, in the comfort of my own home while watching a televised programme about the First World War, I came face to face with Father. A group of war-weary soldiers were struggling towards a raised camera that looked directly at them. They were being led by a bareheaded soldier carrying on his bent shoulders the lifeless body of a comrade The sense of his exhaustion and hopelessness were overpowering as he stumbled towards the camera. He grew closer and clearer, and in those last moments looked directly into the lens.

With a shock of horror that was almost physical I sat bolt upright in my chair, for I was looking into the eyes, burning with hate and anger, of my Father. The oh so familiar lock of hair falling over his forehead was instant confirmation of his identity. I will never ever forget that look of fear and despair on his face, haunted by unspeakable horrors, as he passed out of shot. It took some time for me to digest what I had seen in those brief seconds of Father's life in France. I now understood his pent up anger at the futility of that war and how he had buried it so deeply in his subconscious for so many years. I also understood the reason for my parent's ten year long engagement, as my grandparents would have shown concern about his ability to provide for a family.

Mark and I knew little of Father's illness, as we were protected from the bad periods by Mother. She also did her best to explain the reasons for his breakdown to me, but as a teenager life was black and white. I became resentful towards him, feeling he had refused work by choice and that it had been his duty to stand by his family and put up with any unpleasantness He eventually recovered, but was never fully employed again. With hindsight, perhaps I should have been a little more understanding.

Chapter Fifteen

Our situation deteriorated, as there was now only a small payment from sickness benefit on which to live. Mrs Bell was already snapping at Mother's heels, for she had resented our presence ever since the war had begun. Once again, we were trapped in Tearo House nearly penniless and almost homeless. I am convinced the old house could feel our despair as his creaks and groans seemed to echo our unshed tears of hopelessness. As life would have it, news came that Aunt Barbara was to visit us for a short while. The news was greeted with pleasure and a great deal of apprehension, as visitors incurred extra expenditure. Yet again a trip to the pawn shop was necessary, and preparations began.

The original dining room on the ground floor was a pleasant sunny room with two large windows overlooking the garden and fields beyond. While he was living there, Uncle John had a gas fire installed in the old fireplace, which gave greater comfort. Now, with the bed in one corner, an easy chair, small table and a large cupboard, the room was ready. Father and I were to meet Aunt Barbara, and during our bus journey to the station I was puzzled as to why he seemed nervous about meeting her.

We waited on the platform as the huge locomotive drew to a hissing, steaming halt. Doors clanged open and weary passengers appeared, but suddenly there was a flurry of activity further down the platform. Father stiffened, and I watched in amazement, as a tall angular figure waved a furled umbrella at two porters struggling with a trolley-load of luggage. She approached us, calling in a rich cultured voice, "Ah, there you are Alec, pay the men, will you?" Then, peering anxiously into his face, "And how are you, dear boy?"

Father mumbled his reply, then she turned to me, holding out a gloved hand and saying: "You must be Martha. How do you do?"

I realised then that Granny's sister was a force to be reckoned with, and felt some sympathy for Father's awkwardness.

In spite of her declining years, she proved to be a highly entertaining and amusing house guest, and as she insisted on paying handsomely for her stay, the financial strain was less worrying. Mother was clearly fond of the old lady, and Aunt Barbara's cheerful disposition, satirical sense of humour and deep throaty laugh, lightened the mood of Tearo House considerably.

Aunt Barbara was born in 1875, one of four sisters and two years younger than Granny. They lived on a large farm in Aberdeenshire and Mother recalled spending happy holidays in the magnificent countryside. The four girls were brought up within the strict Presbyterian Church and as a highly determined and independent young woman Aunt Barbara was filled with the ambition to become a Missionary. During the nineteenth century it was deemed unusual for a young lady from a good home to travel alone, but against her parents wishes she set forth for India. It was there she was to spend the greater part of her life, and while doing so met and had long talks with a young Gandhi, who was the inspiration behind the building of many schools and even churches.

She also met and worked alongside the great granddaughter of David Livingstone, thereby forming a lifelong friendship together. As well as this, she wrote books on life in India and was admired and respected by all those who knew her. In short, she was a character.

Chapter Sixteen

I was in my second year at my Grammar School when Aunt Barbara came to visit, and I was growing. The rather sturdy tomboy who happily joined in with her brother's antics was emerging as a tall slender girl. I was also becoming, as Mother explained in her modest, Victorian manner, a 'young lady'. Her mother and daughter talk consisted of the basic facts of the female reproductive system, which in turn led to unfortunate consequences.

Aunt Barbara was a descriptive storyteller and would regale us with breathtaking stories from India. I sat in the kitchen, in the corner by the fire, listening enthralled to tales about Indian palaces and princes:

Coming home from school one day I found my parents in turmoil. Aunt Barbara had had a stroke and was not expected to live. But live she did. It was a slow recovery and tragically she had lost the power of speech. Because of her age, she needed daily nursing and as she was already at Grange Road there was no other alternative than for her to remain. Tearo House smiled as he tightened his grip on the lives of my unfortunate parents. The Missionary Society was contacted and, with Father's help, Aunt Barbara's furnished flat in Ireland was cleared and as many of her belongings that we could accommodate arrived at Grange Road. Power of Attorney was arranged and a weekly amount agreed, and for the first time in Stockdale, Mother had a bank account.

A new routine was established at Tearo House, with Mark and I busy with our school lives and socialising at church, while

Mother and Father looked after Aunt Barbara. She would spend the days in her room, after being washed, changed and fed, then Father would help her down the dangerous little staircase to the kitchen and a warm fire. Although she could not speak, she understood and enjoyed the normal family banter that took place.

At school I was beginning to show an artistic flair, and would proudly show her my paintings. For some reason they caused her great amusement and I learnt to take criticism at an early age.

Now the financial strain had eased, Mother became more relaxed, but the daily grind of looking after her aunt in that difficult house took its toll on her frail body. Before my fifteenth birthday she was taken to hospital for a serious operation, and I was in charge. If life had been normal during the war years Mother would have taught me how to cook, but food was so scarce that she could not afford to waste a single crumb on my training. My only culinary experience was that gained at school and my family were in for a hard time.

I was now mistress of that dreaded scullery, and had to cope with coal deliveries and all the cleaning that ensued. I also needed Father's help on washdays, as I was not as adept as mother with the Poss Tub and heavy hand wringer. The responsibility of caring for my Great Aunt fell heavily on my young shoulders, and mother's faith in my ability to do so was rather optimistic.

Chapter Seventeen

While still in hospital Mother received a letter from her much loved brother Donald. He and his wife Edwina were to drive up to Stockdale to visit her and the family. Mother, thrilled by the news, slightly panicked. I, also excited, completely panicked. I was to host my uncle and his wife, and that meant two things; small talk and food. Sadly, I was inexperienced in both these skills and I began to feel nervous. I had met my Uncle and Edwina only briefly in the past and remembered them as a very glamorous and sophisticated couple.

Armed with explicit instructions from Mother on how to purchase and cook a joint of beef, my confidence returned. After all, what could possibly go wrong? I scrubbed, cleaned and polished the old house, but nothing could disguise the cracked walls, worn carpets and shabby armchairs. To my credit, the brass fender and firearms gleamed brightly in the light of a welcoming fire. I was prepared for a long day and completed Aunt Barbara's ablutions in record time, as she looked forward to seeing her nephew. We had an uproarious time at the hospital, as Mother and Uncle Don fell easily into their childhood banter and Edwina's satirical humour caused not only Father, but other patients, to choke with laughter.

Then home, where I had prepared the table with freshly laundered linen then retired to the scullery.

The vegetables were bubbling merrily and I was ready to make the gravy. I opened the oven door, then gave a strangled scream.

Clouds of smoke billowed around me as I stared in frozen

horror at all that remained of a large piece of beef. My shoulders began to shake as hysterical tears were very near.

Edwina, hearing my scream, appeared at the doorway to the scullery.

"Good God in heaven, Mabs, is this really your kitchen?"

Gazing round the shack she was lost for words.

Then, as the tears flowed, her high heels clattered down the stone steps and a comforting arm wrapped round my shoulders.

"Whatever is the matter, darling?" she drawled in a slightly nasal tone. Then, seeing the burnt offering in my hands, poked it with a scarlet finger and giggled.

"Oh dear, I see. I am afraid all you can do with that is play football. So dry your eyes and we will simply find somewhere else to eat."

By now I was laughing, and we all piled into the car and eventually found a restaurant.

The couple were to visit Mother the next day, before setting off on their long journey south. It was a measure of my uncle's love for his sister to make such an arduous trip in order to spend a few short hours with her.

However, another shock waited for me at the end of that eventful day.

Mother had impressed on me the importance of soaking senna pods in a beaker through the day so as to give the liquid to Aunt Barbara early evening. In the excitement of the day I had forgotten.

I stared blankly at the dried, crumpled pods, almost willing them to produce liquid on their own volition.

What to do? I began to panic.

Gazing desperately around the scullery I spied a bottle of brown liquid. I quickly poured most of the contents over the senna pods, gave the beaker to my Aunt, then hastily left the bedroom.

Later on, during that evening, I casually asked Father to look in on the old lady.

Looking a little surprised at my request, he did so.

All was well and my relief was overwhelming. For the liquid I had given my poor old Aunt was pure vinegar.

It was obvious that Mother was needed at home before I poisoned the whole family.

Chapter Eighteen

After a long recuperation, Mother was finally back in harness, and I am ashamed to say that Father, Mark and myself began to slip back into our usual thoughtless ways. One day, as Doctor Parker carried out his monthly check on Aunt Barbara, he was puzzled by some words she was trying to pronounce. As he had been a medic in India during the last war he thought he recognised words from an obscure dialect only spoken in India. He was deeply interested when Mother told him Aunt Barbara did speak one or two languages, Hindustani being one of them. He then told us that sometimes stroke victims could only speak in the language with which they were most familiar.

Another intrepid traveller to the north was Mrs MacNab, David Livingstone's great-granddaughter. She had been in close contact with my parents during the clearing of Aunt Barbara's flat and now wished to see her good friend. Once more, I found myself in the corner by the fire listening to yet another remarkable old woman recounting tales of their work together, and the people they had met. Mother held a deep-rooted belief in her faith but at that particular time needed Christian comfort and support. So it was as much for Mother's sake that a loving and caring friend travelled so far north.

Mark and I had always been inseparable and as teenagers could read each other's thoughts. We shared our hopes and dreams for the future and only Mark fully understood my romantic yearnings. We dipped our toes into the murky world of adulthood within the confines of the church social life but found most of our companions were slightly older than ourselves. Undeterred, we threw ourselves into our schooldays, where we made friends of our own age.

Swimming sessions at the old Victorian swimming bath were our main enjoyment, and I also visited the cinema regularly with Mother. Teenage life was far less complicated during the 1940s, and Mark and I were content in each other's company.

As we progressed through school it became clear that Mark would almost certainly be offered a place at university, while my artistic skills were of a high enough standard to train at the local Art College. Running true to form in my short life, my dreams were shattered yet again and I had to go out to work. The last weekend in July 1950 saw me leaving school on the Friday, celebrating my sixteenth birthday on Sunday and beginning work on Monday.

Mother did her best to explain why my brothers' careers were more important than mine but I still felt resentful towards Father. Mother contacted a family run publishing company and I was to be their trainee artist earning seven shillings and sixpence a week. I was keen and eager to begin, but pressure of work prevented Mr Cleveland from giving me the promised training and I became frustrated and bored. My misery was plain to see, so Mother took charge again and this time I was to train in a local family run photographic studio. Knowing that I would never be able to follow my dream, this position fulfilled most of my inclinations.

My wage had swollen to eight shillings a week, with the promise of an increase in the future. Mother was relieved.

Now I was working I needed clothes suitable for a working girl, but Mother's budget did not run to finery. So dear old Aunt Barbara's Pandora's Box, in the shape of her trunk from India, was the answer. From it, highly coloured curtains and tablecloths, with the aid of my needle and thread, became fashionable skirts, while gossamer linen provided the frilly petticoats required for the skirt.

I became deeply involved in my work and was showing promise behind the camera. I made friends with a girl slightly older than myself and I was growing, not only in stature, but had more self-confidence towards life in general.

James was doing his National Service and had taken his wings in Canada, while Mark was moving steadily towards university.

49

For the first time since coming north, Mother was enjoying a period of quiet contentment. Then one sad day, during the bitterly cold spring of 1952, Aunt Barbara died.

There was a traditional funeral with the coffin laid out in the room where she had spent the last few years of her life. Mother asked me to say my goodbyes as she lay, resplendent, in her coffin, but I was not quite up to that ordeal.

I remember a cold and rainy day as she was laid to rest. After her departure I was aware of a dreadful sense of loss, but fortunately youth is very resilient.

After Aunt Barbara's sad demise, the small inheritance bestowed on Mother was not enough to compensate for the generous weekly amount she had been receiving.

I now was Mother's only hope. I was due another small increase in my wage, but the burden of my responsibility grew ever heavier.

However, events would take another turn in the shape of a neighbour. He was quiet, polite and had a rather shy smile. He owned his own car and often gave Mother a lift into town. One day he approached me with an invitation to a small gathering at his home.

This seemingly so innocent occasion eventually led to the lives of my beloved family very nearly breaking down.

Chapter Nineteen

There had always been the boy next door.

Tearo House quietly watched and waited during that long hot summer of 1952, smiling malevolently to himself at the despair and heartache that was to follow.

He pursued me with such persistent ardour, that under normal circumstances his affection would have been considered to be thoroughly admirable, but he was not the average boy next door. He was married with two children and was fifteen years older than myself. I was just seventeen and on the brink of life.

My employer, Mr Forsythe, was a tall, balding man with large sensitive hands. He was a mixture of emotional artistry and good business sense and ran his studio by strict Victorian values. I was trained by Mr Forsythe in the specialised skill of hand colouring bromide prints and assisted him in the studio while he taught me the intricacy of lighting.

On one occasion, Mr Forsythe was commissioned by the council to photograph an important building on a main road that was suspected of having bomb damage. I was to assist him, and in order to achieve the correct information we had to stand between fast moving lanes of traffic. This was 1951, long before this digital age, where professional photographers were still using the large 5 x 4 plate cameras and tripod. There we were in the middle of the road with whistles and cat calls from lorry drivers and curious crowds of shoppers beginning to gather on the pavements. Mr Forsythe worked steadily on, oblivious of the crowds and traffic, while I handed him, in strict rotation, the heavy slides.

Desperately trying to cover my embarrassment, I posed and smiled in such a way as to convey to the, by now, laughing crowds that it was absolutely perfectly normal for me to stand in the middle of moving traffic with a man with a large black cloth over his head. Luckily I learned to control my embarrassment on other occasions when working with this absentminded, dedicated craftsman and I was never happier with life. Conversely I was still clinging to Mother for her calming support in much the same way I had done when at school. Every day I walked an extra five miles in order to spend lunch time with her, and when working in Hawksboro I travelled two unnecessary bus journeys for the same reason.

Tearo House seemed to silently mourn the passing of Auntie Babs, and the playroom, by which name it was originally known until housing Uncle John and then Auntie B., once more became the usual unlived in, empty room of earlier years. But at times, tempted by early spring sunshine sparkling through the large windows, I would quietly linger there, thinking my thoughts. I could feel that the room was waiting for something or some one. I knew not what. It was into this life of half child, half woman, came our neighbour Bill.

He was the sixth child of a wealthy local businessman, and a small birth defect meant that his every whim was granted. He had avoided conscription on the grounds of his deformity and his father's insistence that he was needed in the family business. He had been educated at the best of private schools, but did not achieve any outstanding scholastic success due to his embarrassment and shame of his withered foot. After a rebellious and troubled period he eventually married, bought a house in Grange Road and settled down. Or so his parents thought.

Chapter Twenty

It was all so innocent at the beginning. They had always been there, an ordinary family going about their daily business. As they had two small children, they had, very generously, taken another local girl as a babysitter with them on holiday the year before. So, when I was invited to join them on a day at the coast, Mother agreed. Eventually the outings became more frequent and I felt more comfortable with the family. Then there began to be small gifts for Mother from Bill. One day he brought to the house a box of half a dozen fresh farm eggs. This was treasure indeed. Eggs were still rationed and Mother simply could not refuse his generosity.

And so it began. The love affair of the century. Or so I thought. I am sure that if as a family, there had been the usual socialising between cousins, uncles, aunts and grandparents, I would never have given Bill another thought, but I am afraid I did. I became secretive and lied and cheated and betrayed the very people I loved most. I was so completely under his spell that I was incapable of coherent thought, and the inevitable happened. I was pregnant.

I was halfway through my eighteenth year when I had to tell Mother the terrible news. It was the most agonising and painful confession I have ever made in my life. Mother's world fell apart and I was not to know, until much later, the dreadful ramifications my behaviour had caused. Mother managed to calm my hysteria, and for a short while it seemed as if the nightmare was just a bad dream. She insisted that I continued to work as normal, but sadly

I was not aware that Mark had become rather quiet and withdrawn. I was also unaware that Mother almost forcibly prevented Father from killing Bill.

Like most ex-servicemen, he had, tucked away in his old army trunk, a small revolver. Fortunately Mother found it in time and then conveniently lost the weapon. A bitter row ensued and it was only Mark's calming intervention that brought it to a reluctant conclusion.

I continued to keep up the pretence of a carefree teenager at work, but the strain was beginning to show. My slender twenty-two inch waist thickened slightly and rumours began amongst my colleagues. Rumours turned to gossip and then one dreadful day I was summoned to Mr Forsyth's office. His voice was cold and hard. His words were angry, cruel and shocking. I had brought shame and disgrace to his family business and was not fit to work with decent girls. I had to collect my things and leave the premises immediately.

I was distraught. Mother's fury at her life and these narrow-minded and bigoted people hardened and she demanded a meeting with Bill. The outcome being that I was now his responsibility, and that she would nurse and care for me and the child until after the birth when he must find a home for us both.

The next terrible blow came in the form of a note from my elder at church to say I was no longer within her pastoral care and that I would not be welcome at church.

This was the moment when Mother nearly broke down. Her faith and belief in the church had been her lifeline since childhood and this vicious act brought her to tears. As I had been expelled from church, she felt she could no longer face the hostility from this unchristian flock and instead we both attended the church at the top of the road. After tearful phone calls from the telephone box by the Institute to family friend Mrs McNab, Auntie B's beloved friend and colleague was to visit us en route to Scotland. She spent two long evenings with us and we listened intently to her words of such wisdom, love and comfort that we began to feel a little more hopeful for the future.

The second evening they spent together in the playroom, where Mother was able to unburden all her pain, anger and shame at my behaviour. They talked for many hours, then prayed quietly together in the room where Auntie B. had spent the last years of her life and where my baby was to be born some four months hence. Before she left, this by now rather frail old woman, left a gift of a nightgown, hand stitched all by herself, for my unborn child. I was overwhelmed by the feeling of love and caring that came with every stitch in that little garment and I finally broke down.

Her visit gave us the renewed strength that we were to need in the months to follow, for worse was to come.

One day I had walked into town to purchase one or two items for the baby as I was approaching my time. My shopping completed, I began to tire and just had enough change for the bus fare home. In those days service buses had a conductor who would stand on an open platform at the back of the vehicle. This particular day the bus was rather overcrowded, and as it pulled away from the bus stop I had just stepped onto the open platform. Suddenly, I felt a hard hand in the middle of my back determined to push me out of the moving vehicle and into oncoming traffic. I grabbed frantically at the central pole but the driver accelerated and I was losing my grip. It was only the quick thinking conductress who pulled me back onto the safety of the platform that saved me from falling. It was a horrifying thought that somebody living locally wanted to cause me physical harm. But when the anonymous letters arrived, written in an ill-educated hand and with biblical connotations, my parents found it difficult to accept that anybody they knew could do such a thing.

They were vulnerable and defenceless against such bigotry and narrow-minded attitudes and so they carried on with their normal quiet dignity to present a close family unit. As I write this I realise I took almost for granted all the caring, loving and protection I was given by my parents. Being a teenager I was so besotted and embroiled with this elusive man, I was blind to the shame and pain I caused my family. Within their background and strongly held beliefs, I had committed the cardinal sin, but as they felt the wrongdoing was primarily on Bill's side they cared for me as their Christian faith decreed. Without my weekly wage Mother once again faced a hand to mouth existence, but continued to struggle on manfully.

However, there was one small light in her life in the shape of my beloved, gentle, caring Mark. In spite of a truly awful time at school, for even he had experienced animosity and disgust at his sister's behaviour, he had always been there for me with his quietly supportive love. I will always remember the long country walks and talks that we took together during my confinement with deepest gratitude. He was to study at Manchester University the following year and, as it happens, was on the road to becoming one of the country's foremost scientists.

As always, Beth helped with the expenses but, surprisingly and very happily, she had married when in her early fifties and we had not seen her since our last visit to London two years after the war had ended. Numerous telephone calls and weekly letters kept the two sisters together but she was sorely missed.

Chapter Twenty-one

It was on a cold, dark night in November 1953 that my daughter Samantha was born. Mother had dug out of the attic her old bamboo crib that my brothers and myself had used and, with the assistance of Nurse Southall, had transformed the playroom from a bed-sitting room into a nursery. It had been a long labour and I was growing tired. The thin curtains were drawn against the icy rain spattering on the two large windows, and the gas fire was making its usual comforting plopping sounds as I clung onto the high slate mantelshelf with each paralysing labour pain.

My parents were now in the kitchen where Nurse Rainer, a highly skilled and discreet midwife, had ushered my anxious Mother. They clung to each other while praying for a safe delivery as they knew I was nearing my time. Finally Tearo House smiled happily to himself as he heard the angry cry of new life. With the birth of my baby the house seemed to change. It felt more like home with the new routines and extra hustle and bustle that my little bundle caused. Mother began to smile a little more and even Father showed some slight interest. Overall the atmosphere was less tense after a year of such despair.

When Mark came home for the Christmas holidays, my gentle loving brother could not resist the blue eyed, dimpled smile from his niece. Bill, on the other hand, was no stranger to the sentiment that surrounds birth and, on seeing his third daughter, was just able to muster a little enthusiasm, as he had been hoping for a boy.

It was a busy but rather subdued Christmas, brightened by a

fleeting visit from James. Knowing of my situation, he had managed a forty-eight hour pass as he was now flying with BOAC and was working his way to becoming a Captain at an early age. It had been quite some time since last we had seen him and, as we were all adults by now, I felt rather shy with this handsome and imposing brother of mine.

In the past he had been likened to Clark Gable, a well known American heart-throb of that time, and indeed James did have a large dimple in his chin and a lock of thick dark hair did fall over his forehead. James's inscrutable hazel green eyes could look down into your very soul. It transpired that he, too, was involved with affairs of the heart, and was understanding of my position. But in a quiet moment, he told me with a voice like steel, "If ever he hurts you, Mabs, I will kill him."

Mother had her hands full as she cared for me and Sam all through that bitter winter. She guided me carefully through all the bewilderment and confusion that the birth of a child always brings. By the time she thought I was capable of looking after her grandchild, Bill's divorce was nearly completed, but sadly our marriage would not take place until my twenty-first birthday, as Father, in a final act of defiance, refused permission for me to marry.

With the help of his Father, Bill had bought a cottage in a village on the outskirts of Stockdale which was ready for occupation, or so I understood. Finally, with all arrangements completed, one dark day at the end of the winter, and while Father was at work, I tore myself and my baby away from Mother and Tearo House to begin my new life.

As I walked out into the arms of my lover, Mother was alone in that empty house, holding back the tears. I cannot imagine the torment my beloved mother experienced that day. With the wisdom of hindsight I imagine it would have been the lowest point in her life. Her children had gone but the loss of her grandchild was the hardest of all.

She also knew she would have to prepare herself for Father's reaction to her involvement in my departure, knowing there would be anger. And anger there was. Painful, hurtful, distressing anger such as they had never known in their twenty-five years of marriage.

Eventually their emotions subsided and relative peace was restored. They slowly adjusted to a new way of life without their children and even professed to a slight sense of relief. Father took solace in his beloved books, carpentry and tending the garden. Mother persevered with the church, mainly visiting the Church of England at the end of the road. This building was more convenient as the alternative Presbyterian church was well over a mile away. However, neither she nor myself felt comfortable with the Church of England service. She eventually summoned up enough courage to make tentative visits to the closer Presbyterian church and slowly the hostility that had driven her away lessened.

Locally the neighbours became impressed by Mother's sense of decorum and quiet dignity and she even found herself becoming popular, which in private caused her to smile ruefully. One close friend advised her about the possibility of becoming eligible for a retirement bungalow due to the length of her residency in Stockdale. She contacted the council and found to her delight that her name was on the list. Rather strangely, the birth of her grandchild had softened her attitude toward Stockdale and the thought of a smaller home was beyond her wildest dreams.

Meanwhile, back in London, it was Beth who had reached a crisis point in her life. Although she had married late in life, she had continued to work and still care for Granny. Tragedy struck when her husband had a severe stroke and she had no other choice than to ask for help from her sister. Hurried arrangements were made for Granny to be safely brought to the north, and within the week she was home in Stockdale. How strange it was for Granny to find herself in the same house, under the same care and in the same room where her sister had lived not so very long ago. Tearo House once more found himself smiling at the love that sisters share between each other, and marvelled at the strength it brings.

It was hard work for my parents, but this time Father helped with the carrying of food from the scullery to the playroom, once again disguised as a bed-sitting room. However, Granny's generous contribution towards the household expenses was such a relief for Mother that she willingly cared for her ageing parent.

After my abrupt departure Mother promised Father, rather unreasonably she thought, not to visit me as he felt it would condone my 'living in sin'. So during this time we saw very little of each other.

Not to be outdone, we met occasionally in town, thereby keeping in touch whilst knowing it would not be long before my marriage.

Chapter Twenty-two

I contemplated my new life with some trepidation, which was instantly quashed as I was still drunk with love for the man who was the father of my child.

The cottage was situated at the bottom of a steep hill leading to a row of six, originally built for the workers on the estate of Harrow Hall. This was the stately home round which the village of Harrowby evolved. A garden path, flanked on either side by waist-high hedges, led to the heavy front door of the middle cottage. To the left of the door, climbing roses draped themselves confidently round a long narrow window. I gasped with surprise when entering my new home, for it was indeed rather old. It was what was commonly known as a 'one up, one down' with one or two refinements. The inordinately large living room sported oak beams in a low ceiling with an attractive inglenook fireplace. A coal fire with back boiler to heat the building and water, replaced the original open fire. Stepladder type stairs originally accessed the bedroom but had been blocked in with only a single hand rail for support. Partitioned off from the bedroom, a bath and small hand basin had been hurriedly installed, leaving open pipes and a splintery wood floor.

The stone floored kitchen contained the dreaded stone Belfast sink, a dangerous looking gas stove and a large wood topped kitchen table. As I gazed disconsolately round this cold bare room I realised that a necessary component to comfortable living was missing. I flung open the creaking back door to be greeted by stone flags leading across a muddy patch of grass (the garden, I

60

supposed) to a red brick cubicle housing a fully flushing water closet. My immense relief at discovering a flushing lavatory was immediately dashed by the realisation of the appalling inconvenience this would bring. I was also later to discover that only a muddy lane, wide enough to accommodate Mr Stringer's horse and cart when delivering his bags of coal, separated the small back garden from a snuffling, snorting overwhelmingly pungent pig farm.

Happily, at this point in my life, I was still so young, bewitched and dazzled by this man, who professed to love me above all others, that I could laughingly cope with an outside lavatory, which invariably froze during the winters. I was also able to cope with only a poss-stick and large tub with which to do the family washing. I might add that I still use the same poss-stick on odd occasions, sixty-five years later. But when the erratic coal deliveries left me, with my baby, shivering, without heat or hot water, I was not quite so understanding.

We settled down to an uneasy routine, whereby Bill would go to work with his father in town, return for his supper, then enjoy the rest of the evening at the village pub. He made it clear that, if I was not happy with the arrangement, I was free to leave.

During the 1950s, social barriers were beginning to break down but the country still retained many of the old Victorian values. Racism was rampant; the establishment still ruled, homosexuality and abortion were punishable by law, divorce was frowned upon and illegitimacy ostracised one for life. A single woman with a child and no visible means of either financial or family support could find herself in an institution for unmarried mothers.

When Bill and I finally married, Mother breathed a huge sigh of relief, for I was unaware of how precarious my position had become. I suspect it was only Bill's deep admiration for my indomitable mother, tinged with a little fear, that brought him to the altar.

Time had passed, and my twenty-first birthday was fast approaching. Bill gave me money with which to buy my wedding outfit, and mindful that my fall from grace had excluded virginal white, I chose a grey light wool suit, white lace blouse and a white half hat, fashionable at that time.

I was to carry a white leather-bound prayer book, which with a pair of pillowcases from Granny, had been my only wedding gift. As I was 5 foot 7 inches tall and weighed 9 stone, I was considered to be quite attractive, but there was no one there that day to whisper loving compliments except Mark, who on first seeing me, paused momentarily, then with his special smile simply said, "Hello Mabs, you're looking good." I, in turn, was taken aback by this elegant university student, suited and booted for the occasion, who only yesterday, it seemed, had been my baby brother. Even Samantha was resplendent in a new frock and shoes.

Bill looked handsome in an expensive sports jacket with well cut trousers. The age gap between us was obvious and I never fully understood why he had pursued me so determinedly, but the phrase 'Trophy Wife' tends to come to mind occasionally. He was a complex and difficult man to understand, but I loved him with all the enthusiasm I might have bestowed on a challenging puppy. However, Bill was not to be trained.

The day of our wedding dawned grey and cloudy, even though the month was August. When Bill left to pick up three buttonholes and Mark, I sat in that dark little cottage cradling Samantha in my arms and knew I was about to make the worst mistake of my life. I was too young to make this lifelong commitment but I had to protect Samantha from the stigma of illegitimacy. So it was with a heavy heart that I set out for my wedding that dreary August day.

The ceremony took place in a small country Registry Office and two complete strangers were brought in to be our witnesses. As we stood before the Registrar, listening to those age-old words, I searched Bill's face for some kind of emotion, some small sign of love, but his eyes could not meet mine and his features remained as inscrutable as ever.

The ceremony was over in what seemed a heartbreakingly short time and all I longed for was to feel Samantha's soft little body in my arms. She waited patiently in the car while our nuptials were taking place, and afterwards Bill had booked a table at a large hotel on the coast. Mark and I were slightly overawed at the splendour of the dining room and Samantha behaved impeccably. Bill finally began to relax, and as the meal progressed the wine began to flow. Mark and I took a little, but Bill was a hardened drinker and his mood changed from rather drunken anecdotes to truculent complaints about the food and the service. I had had enough to drink to enable me to retaliate, and so what had begun as a pleasant meal ended in angry words.

We left the hotel and drove in silence to the cottage. More angry words were exchanged, and Bill drove off leaving me with Samantha and an embarrassed and unhappy Mark.

I changed out of my finery, fed and bathed Samantha who, after a bedtime story read by Uncle Mark, settled happily down to sleep. And so it was my beloved brother who waited quietly with me during my wedding evening, until reluctantly leaving for the last bus home.

Bill had an unfortunate habit of collecting, then tiring of and discarding, various dogs and cats and so I busied myself by sweeping up dog hair on my hands and knees while waiting for my new husband to return.

Meanwhile, back at Tearo House, my parents had settled down to a relatively contented routine. Surprisingly, Father had found a somewhat lowly position in a small office in town, during which he had been summoned to Jury Service at Durham Law Courts. These events seemed to help with his self-esteem, and as Mother could now afford to buy tobacco for his well-worn pipes he was more contented with his lot. Mother, in turn, had found a group of new and stimulating friends, and as I was now married she was able to put the past behind her.

Mrs Bell continued to be her usual disagreeable self, but as the rent was now paid on a regular basis, she had no real reason for complaint.

Mark came home from university during his holidays and took on holiday work, thereby bringing fresh life into the old house. James was having a rather turbulent time with affairs of the heart, and Beth was struggling to rehabilitate her poor sick husband.

Mr Robinson's much loved old horse, Betty, was long gone, but the old man still fattened up the usual bunch of turkeys for Christmas.

Chapter Twenty-three

My second child was due to be born in May and I was feeling lonely. For quite some time Bill had been dissatisfied with his work in his father's business, and after a great deal of discussion between architects and solicitors, Bill's father agreed to utilise some property he owned so that Bill could open his very own paint and body workshop. He threw himself wholeheartedly into setting up the business, declaring that because of his love for internal combustion, this had been his dream. His enthusiasm was quite touching, but when problems arose he became petulant and self-pitying, inevitably laying the blame on his disability.

To alleviate my loneliness I told Bill I was taking the country bus with Samantha to town to meet Mother for coffee at least once a week. As he was so involved with the business, he was quite agreeable as long as his supper would be ready for his homecoming. Then, one day, when Father was carrying out Jury Service, Mother felt it was time for me to return to Tearo House. I said nothing of my plans to Bill, as this was between Mother and myself. As I stepped into the so familiar hall, with the dark linoleum and threadbare strip of carpet, all I could say was, "Oh, Mum."

Her reply was as brief! "Well, Mabs."

We did not embrace but a long look passed between us. I knew she would give her life for me if necessary, but I had cheated and lied to her. As she believed marriage was for life, and divorce and illegitimacy were unthinkable, coming to terms with my behaviour had been a long path to tread. Then the moment was over and it was as if I had never left.

We took Samantha to meet her great-grandmother, who was by now a frail eighty-five year old. Propped against her pillows, her silver white hair forming a halo around her face, she was the picture of dignified fragility.

Down in the kitchen nothing had changed. The same lumpy armchairs in front of a welcoming fire. The same chestnut coloured chenille cloth over the wood table top with the same Dresden figurine resplendent in the middle. This was the table where Mother would empty her purse of coins and I would catch them as they rolled out. If, when counted into their various piles, they were insufficient for the necessary bills, she would sigh wearily, and I knew, with dread in my heart, it meant another visit to the pawn shop.

The fear and shame that Mother had felt at never quite having enough money on which to live had seeped through to my very bones and remained with me for life. As fate would have it, I was to experience similar problems, but for different reasons, within my own marriage. As my pregnancy progressed I became a regular visitor to Grange Road. The air of calm orderliness that now pervaded Tearo House made a welcome break from the physical and emotional chaos that was my life at the cottage. Father's attitude towards Bill was slowly mellowing and barriers were breaking down.

One day I left Samantha with Mother in order to purchase a small item for my baby in town. Enjoying the simple freedom, I decided to surprise Bill at the garage. To my horror I found my new husband in a passionate embrace with his young and giggling secretary.

A terrible row ensued, but eventually other arrangements were made to cope with the office side of the business. I was deeply unhappy, for I trusted Bill implicitly, but I was also aware of his womanising reputation.

I said nothing to Mother and hid my misery well, but I am sure she sensed something was wrong.

The winter dragged on and I took to walking the narrow lanes around the village with Sam in her unwieldy pushchair. I imagine I made a lonely figure, with my equally lonely child, as I trudged through the bare hedgerows desperately looking for signs of spring, for spring would bring not only the lambs, but my own newborn child. Then one morning, half way through April, I felt decidedly unwell. The restless, uneasy feeling continued and my head began to ache. As I had seen the doctor only three times during the last eight months I felt I needed to be checked over. With Samantha in her pushchair, I struggled round to the large house where my doctor lived and held his surgery.

He was a tall, distinguished looking man with a courtly manner, who had recently retired from his position as Surgeon at a large hospital in a nearby town. On examination he found that the baby was lying in the breech position, but said, as I had a full three weeks to go before the birth date, the foetus would turn naturally and there was no cause for concern. His confident manner calmed me and I returned home to spend a restless day and night.

The next day Bill left for work as usual, telling me not to worry. But as the day wore on, my condition worsened. I began to vomit and my head felt as if it would burst. I wanted to speak to Bill, but the one and only public telephone box was on the other side of the village and I was weary. As I had nothing for supper that night a visit to the butcher was the answer. He was a cheerful person, with large hands and a large voice, and we exchanged the usual pleasantries until my purchase was completed.

The walk down the hill was less arduous than walking up with Samantha's small wheeled and cumbersome pushchair, but even so I longed to get home. On the way I met my midwife, who gave me a long searching look and said she would examine me there and then. I thought of the chaos I had left behind, unwashed breakfast dishes, unruly dogs and cats to be fed, and my vomit to clean up. Disregarding my now near to tears embarrassment at the state of the cottage, she simply rolled up her sleeves and took charge. Within the hour the animals had been seen to, Samantha was asleep and I, with a hot cup of tea, had instructions to rest as much as I could.

Bill returned home ready for his supper, and after listening to the events of my day he left for the pub. After bathing Samantha and reading her a bedtime story I began to feel the pains. I had three weeks to go and this was not normal. Panic set in and I wanted my mother but I had to wait for Bill to return.

Fortunately he returned a little earlier that night, to be confronted by a groaning, sweating and furious wife. "Go and get the midwife," I spat out between gasps and gritted teeth. Obviously Bill was slightly drunk, and as he disappeared into the dark night I wondered if I would ever see him again.

He did return, not with the midwife but with the butcher. As he swayed in front of me, proudly declaring he had brought help, I screamed:

"I don't want the butcher, I want the bloody midwife!"

Bill had gone to the wrong cottage and the butcher had offered to help an out-of-control father to be.

However, this gentleman proved to be helpful after all, as I could not get up the narrow staircase that had the incline of a stepladder. His strong arms made a kind of sling whereby I could put my weight on his chest, and with Bill supporting him from behind, somehow, with a great degree of groaning grunting and swearing from the three of us, they managed to support me up that awful stairway and finally into the sanctuary of the bed. By now Bill was beginning to sober up at the realisation of the seriousness of my condition, and finally came back with the midwife.

"I thought I might see you tonight," she smiled gently, as I was by now becoming rather distressed.

She took control immediately and my feeling of panic subsided. With her calm voice and soothing hands she administered gas and air for pain relief, organised Bill with tea making and began to time my labour pains. Minutes ticked by, but minutes became hours and nothing was happening. The pain was intensifying and I was weary. Nurse Southall was worried. Strands of whispery grey hair escaped from under her little blue cap and her voice was tense as she ordered Bill to fetch Doctor Bennet.

On arrival, the doctor examined me and his face was grim. I had held the nurse's hand with each pain, but when she explained to the doctor that my grip was painful he barked: "Tie a towel to the bed rail, we have nothing else to give her." The tension in the room was mounting. He smiled apologetically and said, "The old remedies are always the best, I find."

Doctor and nurse talked quietly together and I remember pleading, "When will it be over?"

Then suddenly their voices were loud and urgent.

"Push!" the nurse commanded. "Push again, push harder!" I heard a loud whooshing sound, and their aprons and hands and even faces were spattered with blood.

From a distance I could hear what sounded like running water and they were shouting at Bill to bring more buckets, bowls, anything to hold the blood. Their voices were beginning to fade as I heard "It's a boy."

Thank God, I thought, as soft, dreamy, wonderful sleep washed over me, when suddenly SMACK, a man's heavy hand dealt a blow, such a blow, first to one side of my face and then to the other. I struggled painfully to sit up, blazing with furious anger. "How dare you hit me?" I shouted with as much energy and dignity I could muster. "How dare you, nobody hits me. How dare you!"

His voice was harsh with emotion. "Live, woman, live. You have your boy, that's all you wanted, now wake up and live."

I began to cry tears of exhaustion, and the sound of running water began to slow down. Nurse Southall handed me a large bundle with a gentle smile. Doctor Bennett, suddenly exhausted, sat down on a chair near the dressing table and picked up my white prayer book. "Everywhere I go I see one of these," he said scathingly. "What good did your God do for you? Don't you realise you nearly died tonight?"

What is the man talking about, I thought, as finally I drifted gently into blessed, dreamless sleep.

Chapter Twenty-four

The next morning Bill, with a tearful Samantha, knocked at the door of Tearo House. Mother was shocked to hear of her grandson's early arrival, but Samantha was now her priority. Unknown to Mother, Tearo House was about to receive another very welcome and surprising visitor.

Nurse Southall arrived early next morning, her tired eyes showing the strain of the night before, but the blue cap was firmly pulled over her hair and the crisp white apron crackled reassuringly. "How are we today?" she greeted me cheerily.

"I am fine, thank you," I replied. "But I have a lot of questions to be answered."

As she carried out her nursing duties, she began by explaining that both I and my baby must have the constitutions of an ox to have survived the ordeal. It was due only to the experience and expertise of Doctor Bennett that my life was saved. She told me that they had not been prepared for such a serious birth and had nothing with which to help either them or myself. She described the birth as a double breech by which feet and bottom present first. The risk to the baby was that he might either choke or the neck would break. She paused thoughtfully.

"And then you haemorrhaged. . ." she paused again, before continuing: "You must realise, Mrs Carter, we had nothing. No drugs, no machines and we were losing you. And so he hit you, very hard, it was all he could do to stop you slipping away, and luckily it worked." She then explained that if my baby had gone full time he would certainly have killed me as his weight was a hefty nine pounds and four ounces at three weeks' premature. I wanted to know why he was such a peculiar colour, as he was purple up to his arm pits and his legs looked as if they were attached to his chest. I was told this was due to his surviving such a traumatic birth and that eventually the bruising would clear and his legs grow strong and straight.

Together, with time, we slowly recovered and I was my usual strong self again. However, two days later, when still confined to bed, I had a wonderful surprise. Bill had gone to work as usual, leaving me in the dubious care of a woman from the village who called in twice a day to make me a cup of tea, when I heard a familiar voice calling, "Are you up there, Mabs?" Imagine my surprise when, not only James appeared, but he had brought his future bride. As I had only just given birth, neither I nor my home were at our best. They were the personification of sophistication.

James grew more handsome with the passing years. There was a mature confidence and an air of commanding authority about him and I felt a little shy with this almost stranger. His clothes were casual but of the quality only to be had in London. Tall and lean, he was very much the man about town. Katherine was a handsome looking girl, dark eyes with thick short hair, and her commanding voice was not to be ignored. Her apparel also, was simple, elegant and expensive. They were so out of place in that shabby bedroom as to be likened to two butterflies on a dung heap. There were still signs of the eventful night before, with soiled linen in one corner and all the paraphernalia of baby care items strewn around.

I could hear the animals running amok in the living room, with the occasional crash of broken china. Fortunately, my two-day-old son, all crumpled, misshapen and plumb coloured, slept peacefully in his crib. I desperately tried to tidy my, by now, not so clean bed while tugging at my matted hair and wishing I could simply disappear. James, realising my embarrassment, did his best to put me at my ease, as too did Katherine, but it was not quite the way I wished to first meet my sophisticated sister-in-law.

They were staying at Tearo House while James showed Katherine the glory of the north, and would be gone within a few days. During her stay Katherine was sleeping in the playroom while James was in his old room, of course. Mother would never, under any circumstances, condone shared sleeping arrangements under her roof, so it was fortunate that the playroom was a spare bed-sitting room once again.

Slowly the after effects of Robert's traumatic birth faded away and he grew into a blue eyed, red headed, mischievous dumpling. I continued to visit Mother one day every week and we grew closer than ever, both of us delighting in my children. It was a special time for us and Mother began to realise she was putting down roots in Stockdale. With the promise of a two-bedroomed easy care, pensioners' bungalow as their new home she hoped that she and Father could put the past behind them and settle down with their grandchildren. I hoped and prayed they would remain, but the pull of their roots was perhaps too strong and neither of us could foresee the future.

The soft spring sunshine filtered through the drawn curtains of a large, well furnished bedroom. Clutching my year old baby in my arms, I stared nervously down at the face of an old woman in her coffin. I was twenty-two years old and had not seen a dead person, but my elderly sister-in-law standing by my side had insisted. For this was my mother-in-law.

I squirmed with embarrassment as I felt it was an insensitive intrusion into her death, but Bill's family, in their wisdom, had kept his shameful divorce and remarriage from her. For some strange reason his father, whom I had met but once, had insisted that I, with our son, attend the funeral. The day came and Bill proved to be little support, leaving me on my own almost from the beginning. I was intimidated by these people with their confident voices and expensive clothes, and knowing we were related by marriage. Cold eyes looked me up and down, then backs turned and I was ignored. Mrs Carter's funeral was well attended and the service dragged on longer than usual, or so it seemed.

I was irritated by Bill's lack of support and we left long before the party was over.

During the years to follow it became clear that Bill did not socialise. Once or twice one of his brothers had invited us to a small family party, but Bill would refuse with a polite excuse, leaving me in tears of disappointment and his sister-in-law angered by his bad manners. His elder spinster sister, Annie,

71

would occasionally call unannounced and I did my best to befriend her, but with nearly a generational gap between us there was little common ground. Bill was only comfortable in the 'Hail Fellow, Well Met' atmosphere of either a country or town public house.

Bill had always had a tendency to bring home strange animals, from a monkey to a fox, but late one night at the cottage he arrived home with two strangers. They were, according to their intoxicated giggles, long lost friends of Bill's and were surprised to find him living in this delightful village. Our friendship with Jilly and Frank lasted nearly ten great years until very suddenly Frank died. It was a terrible shock to us all and he left a large gap in our lives.

Jilly and Frank had married late in life and were childless. Frank was a reporter with the local newspaper and occasionally Jilly would accompany him on various assignments. Frank was a plain looking man, but his quick wit and sardonic sense of humour were particularly endearing. It was an unbalanced friendship as I was the house 'frau', tied to the home by the strict routine I had in bringing up my children, whereas Bill, Jilly and Frank were free to party at their will. However, they respected my principles and were content to spend late evenings with me after meeting up in the pub with Bill. At first our times together were on a casual basis, but as the friendship deepened the evenings were prearranged.

I loved these times, as I would scrub and polish until my cottage sparkled, then prepare dainty little nibbles to wash down the beer and my Babychams. I suspected that Jilly and Frank had been intrigued by the notoriety of Bill's divorce when finding us living in that little cottage tucked away in a corner of the village so far from Stockdale. For notorious we had been. Bill was known as the problem son of a highly respected and wealthy businessman in town and as such easy prey to any gossip or scandal, true or false.

Chapter Twenty-five

When we first moved to the village, Bill was still paying alimony to his first wife and allowance to his children, leaving very little over for his new family. Our home was furnished by items bought by Bill from the local sale rooms. His father very generously gave us a large oak dining table and dresser, but anything further that was needed had to come from the small allowance I was given each week. We needed curtains for the living room, so I diligently saved for many weeks until I reached my target. There was a small haberdashery in the village main street which could have been straight out of 'Cranford'.

This was new territory to me and disappointingly I could only afford a length of curtain material to be made up at home on my machine. This I did, and spent two days hand stitching one hundred curtain rings to the top hem. I had no idea as to how to hang them, so in sheer desperation and aided by a hammer, three nails and a strong piece of string, the job was done.

It was the autumn of 1956 when I first met Jilly and Frank and was flattered by their seeming enjoyment of the evenings spent in our humble home. As the weather grew colder they welcomed the warmth of an open fire. Our large living room was lit by two small lamps and the firelight flickering on the old beams in the low ceiling. With the, by now, sagging curtains, drawn against the dark night and the lumpy horsehair chaise longue pulled in front of the inglenook fireplace, our quirky little cottage was indeed conducive to merrymaking. And much merriment was made that year, as Bill had bought a firkin of beer for Christmas. It sat in

d

splendour on a shelf in the pantry adjoining the living room. Huge hooks hung from the ceiling beams from which venison or hams would be hung. The floor was laid with original red quarry tiles and Bill's firkin did not look amiss in that icy cold room.

Bill was a generous host and Jilly and Frank were highly delighted when invited to pull their own drinks. As the evenings progressed and the trips to the pantry increased, the laughter would become suggestive and the legs a little unsteady, but when confronted by the comforts of our outdoor privy, the humour was decidedly lavatorial in content. Jilly was a keen DIY enthusiast, and one evening, when they were in their cups, she took Bill to task about the curtains. She praised me for my ingenuity, while explaining the wonders of curtain wire, then laughingly admonished Bill for leaving me to cope on my own.

Many happy hours were spent in our little cottage but I was still young and I wanted parties and dancing amid meeting people. Jilly was a friend, but although she was younger than Bill and Frank, she was still much older than myself, and I would have liked to have someone of my own age to share my kind of silliness.

When spring began to melt into summer I took my sketch book with my babies in their heavy pram and searched the country lanes for subjects to sketch and paint. As I began to fill my books, the unrest I had felt during the winter began to ease, but I made the mistake of showing Bill some of my artwork. For the next day I found the word DIRT written on what was admittedly a dusty surface. From then on, I resolved to keep my work to myself.

Samantha was growing up and Bill was concerned about the standard of teaching in the village schools. He also found the daily travelling between home and business rather tiring, so he decided we should move back to town. My new home was bought and the cottage sold without any consultation, or even consideration, as to my likes or dislikes on any of these matters. On reflection, and by today's standards, this would be unheard of, but in those days, unless a woman had money of her own, she was completely dependant on her husband's charity. So I was told not to worry and that Bill had the matter in hand, which, of course, he had.

I first saw my new home two weeks before we were due to move in, and found it difficult to hide my disappointment. It was in what was considered to be a good area, in a cul-de-sac opposite

Stockdale's municipal park. Samantha's school was a twenty minute walk away and it was also within walking distance of Tearo House, albeit a long walk; but I was young and strong. The house was terraced, it had three bedrooms, two reception and, to my horror, a narrow back yard that opened onto a communal back street where women could hang out their washing. It was spring 1957 when we moved into this large house, with very little furniture and even less in the way of carpeting. As always I remained positive and was happy to be within reach of my parents. This was all that really mattered, as they could now watch their grandchildren grow and mature.

In the meanwhile, my parents had met another couple who came from a part of London they knew well. Not only that, but Mother was on such good terms with the new vicar she was able to approach him about a very personal matter. As Samantha and Robert had not yet been christened she was thrilled when he agreed to perform a Christening Service at Tearo House.

It was held in the playroom with Granny attending, and proved to be a very moving ceremony. Once again, Tearo House had played host to a very important part of my life.

Mark was going from strength to strength at university and was studying for his doctorate. While doing so he applied for an important position at a well known chemical company which, if he was successful, would involve him signing The Official Secrets Act. This meant that not only his parents but grandparents and great-grandparents had to be vetted by Special Branch. Mother was highly flattered when my parents were praised by these policemen as to Mark's impressive pedigree.

Sadly, some months later, Granny died peacefully in her sleep. It was to be expected as she was a frail eighty-five year old, but her passing brought a great sadness to all our lives. Tearo House shared in our sorrow, as the empty playroom made its presence felt more than any other empty room, but happily this was soon to change.

While at university Mark met Prunella, another student. Her home town was Leeds, where her father was a well known General Practitioner, and they seemed to be very much in love. Whenever the young couple had a break from their studies they would come north and Prue would sleep in the playroom, thereby restoring the balance of life in the old house again. I would walk from Lilac Grove to spend the days with them and loved to watch Prue in the sunny room while sitting at the dressing table to brush her waist long hair. This would then be tied into a large knot and pinned on top of her head. With her expensive spectacles in place, I deeply envied her youthful, intellectual appearance.

When she failed her degree, perversely, she began to pursue Mark with the relentless determination of a girl whose father had granted her every wish. Poor Mark, bewildered, confused and worn down by her overwhelmingly feminine wiles, eventually conceded defeat.

The university was horrified by his disastrous decision and wrote several times to my parents in the hope they could persuade him to change his mind, but to no avail. Apparently he was their most gifted student, and as such a good example for the university's reputation.

My thoughtful, caring brother was no match for a woman as obsessed by marriage as Prue. So a date was set and I, with my parents, Sam and Robbie, attended the wedding, which was more like a celebrity event where Mark had to play his part, instead of a religious service. I watched his strained white face all through that long day, knowing that he was already regretting his decision.

It proved to be a turbulent marriage, as was both mine and James's, but for the three of us our children were all that mattered.

As the years passed by, even though we were separated by distance, I grew quite close to Prue. But Mother and I knew that both the boys had chosen the wrong girl as their lifelong partners. As indeed, had I chosen the wrong man. I often wondered why it was that we three children, who were so loved, had made such bad choices in our partners. Prue was a determined young woman and expected the good life within her marriage.

Chapter Twenty-six

The house in Lilac Grove was reminiscent of Grange Road apart from the complete lack of foliage of any description, and it bothered me. All that I had ever known were lush gardens and open fields, so this world of brick and concrete proved to be challenging. The two reception rooms were high ceilinged with large windows. There was a walk-in pantry adjoining a small square room with a kitchen range and scullery. This was narrow and dark, with the usual stone Belfast sink, and I wondered miserably whether I would ever be free from the drudgery of these stone sinks.

We had very little in the way of furnishings, but slowly occasional items would arrive, either bought by Bill or rejects from his old home, which very conveniently was quite close by. Eventually the house was furnished with the barest of necessities and I did my best to make it a home. Jilly and Frank were delighted with our return from the country and we began to see more of them.

Although Lilac Grove did not have the intriguing atmosphere of the cottage, our home still managed to retain a certain quirkiness. This was partly due to Bill's older sister Annie, as she had an unfortunate addiction to furniture sale rooms.

She would attend every local sale, thereby making undesirable purchases which were then housed in our home. Annie was unmarried and lived with her father who would not understand her unnecessary expenditure. Consequently I spent much time moving furniture around in order to accommodate such items as an Indian totem pole or a ferocious looking stuffed Golden Eagle. These items may make an interesting talking point but I certainly did not want them in my sitting room. One day, when a large wooden organ complete with bench arrived, I felt she had gone too far.

These items would eventually be sold on, but some would linger longer than others, much to my irritation.

Not long after moving to Lilac Grove, Bill built a couple of hutches wherein to keep rabbits and guinea pigs as well as our large dog and two cats. As always, the novelty wore off and I was left to care for them. It was clear that Bill shared his sister's passion for acquiring unwanted items simply to discard them at a later date. My breaking point with Annie was the organ, but with Bill it was in the shape of Old Bob. It was the usual story of how he had met a man in the pub who wanted to sell his dog. Old Bob was a magnificent Old English Mastiff. He was huge and his size could be rather off-putting but he was a gentle old boy. He had an open sore on his right flank which the owner said would not heal and Bill saw this as a challenge.

This huge animal was brought to live in a house with two children and only a small back yard in which to stretch his legs. A dog of this size obviously needed a lot of exercise, but Bill never had time to walk it. As the house was in a cul-de-sac, I, with my friends, would leave our front doors unlocked for the children to run in and out while playing together. I did my best to make sure the door was always closed but understandably there were times when it was not. Bob being Bob, simply did as he wished and took every opportunity to go walk about. At first he was content to play with the children in the avenue, but it did not take him long to discover the park, where he was in his element. It appears he had a penchant for sweet smelling flowers and would roll his great body over and over in sheer delight in the most expensive flower displays the park gardeners had created. Time after time, I would open my front door only to find an apoplectic park keeper holding Old Bob by the collar and threatening me with everything from fines to imprisonment.

Bill was highly amused by Old Bob's adventures in the park and told me to ignore the park keeper, but when I was faced by the furious man yet again I began to lose my temper.

One hot day, when the children were playing with their friends and I was busy with my sewing machine on the kitchen table, Old Bob lay underneath panting wearily with the heat. I had opened the kitchen window and the scullery door in the hope that a draft might help the retched animal. Suddenly and explosively he vomited an enormous squirming, wriggling disgustingly alive ball of worms. As I gazed in horror at the obscene mass, a huge slimy tape worm detached itself from the ball and began to slither towards my foot.

It was the very stuff of nightmares and sadly meant that poor Old Bob would have to go.

While living in the avenue I became acquainted with a group of women who were to be my firm friends. They were slightly older than myself and came from different backgrounds, but as we were all mothers we had a lot in common. We supported each other with all the problems of child rearing and the art of home making, and in doing so grew close in the understanding of each other's likes and dislikes. We began to meet one evening a week on a rota system in each other's homes where, free from the needs of children, we could put the world to rights. Not only did I get to know these women very well but I was able to study their relationships with their husbands. What I saw was quite revealing. Without exception, each woman was treated with respect, companionship, trust and above all, faithful love. I could see quite clearly that my marriage contained none of these normal emotions. I was young enough to feel I loved him, but it was more a sense of gratitude for caring for me and guilt at my past misdemeanours. The shame and guilt I experienced as a naïve and so innocent teenager nearly destroyed me, so I was easy prey for Bill. His controlling nature sensed my fear but he could see no wrong in his actions.

On one particular night he was feeling amorous, but I was rather tired and tried carefully to avoid his embraces. I knew it was unwise but he persisted. The more I resisted the angrier he became, until the final coupling ended in a violent and degrading struggle. I had neither heard of nor read about marital rape but I was beginning to realise that my marriage to Bill bore no resemblance to that of my friends.

Six weeks later I knew I was pregnant, and although shocked was happy about the forthcoming birth. As my pregnancy progressed, Bill became withdrawn and irritable and I was confused as to his change of mood. One day, when Annie called to tell me that two old carver chairs would be arriving and that I could keep them for an indefinite period of time, I was very pleased and thanked her profusely, but then she approached the subject of my pregnancy. It was plain from her manner that Bill had hinted that it was due to my over active maternal instincts and that he was desperately worried about all the extra cost of another child.

As my pregnancy progressed I began to feel unwell. I had always suffered morning sickness but this time it was different. Mother was concerned about my condition as even the usual medication did nothing to relieve the symptoms. I was also simmering with resentment about Bill's version of the conception of the child. Dragged down by anger and illness, Bill sensed my depression and began to slowly persuade me that it would be better all round to terminate the pregnancy. I was horrified. All those years ago when he had tried to abort Samantha I had fully agreed but not this time. However, when my back began to ache continually, I finally gave in.

With the greatest regret and worn down by the situation, I took the pills that Bill gave me. Two a day for four days, but after two days I began to feel unwell. Then I became so ill that I collapsed and Bill had to call out a doctor. He was a new young doctor, and after examining me, began to ask disturbing questions. This was 1959, and abortion was illegal, so I became alarmed at the way his questioning was going. He asked whether I had taken anything. I played innocent, not understanding the question. He was standing in our sparsely furnished bedroom, one arm resting on the high mantelshelf of the fireplace, and he repeated the question. His voice was gentle but his mood was changing.

I replied shakily that Bill had given me something for morning sickness. He asked to see the pills. I flatly refused. It was then he nearly lost control and slammed his fist down hard on the mantelshelf. "Don't you know I could send your husband to prison?" he thundered. "In fact, he deserves to go to prison for what he has done to you. Don't you realise you are desperately ill and your system is closing down. I need to see these pills in order to give you the correct antidote."

Tearfully, I begged him to promise not to imprison Bill and then I would show him what I had taken. He called me, amongst many other names, 'a very stupid young woman', but reluctantly agreed to my request.

Within the hour I had taken the antidote and was ordered to take twenty-four hour bed rest.

Mother came to care for the children until I was on my feet again. She stayed on for a while longer as she was a tower of strength, both for Bill and myself, and was never to know the real cause of my illness. I was too ashamed.

Chapter Twenty-seven

The winter dragged on long and hard as they are in the north, and at times Lilac Grove seemed to be almost as cold as Tearo House.

The kitchen and scullery, where I spent most of my time, although cramped, were quite cosy with a blazing coal fire in the old range.

As the morning sickness and backache continued, I made the long walk to the surgery. I saw the Senior Partner, a wise old Scotsman, who told me there was a new drug on the market but he was uneasy about its reputation and would not prescribe it for me.

I had the choice of making another appointment if I so wished, but, at that moment in time, I was too weary to make the long journey again. I often dwell on my decision not to take that drug, for if I had my beautiful healthy baby would have been born with the most appalling abnormalities. The drug was Thalidomide.

With the arrival of spring the weather improved rapidly and I began to feel a little better. The outlook was good so, as a thank you to Mother for all her help when I was so ill, Bill booked a holiday on the Norfolk Broads.

Father was happy to stay with his sister for the week, so Mother looked forward to the new experience. Our cruiser was exceptionally comfortable and Mother was happy with her cabin. The children were thrilled to have Nana with us for the whole week and each day brought a different mooring place in which to stay, with fresh excitements to explore. From the moment we arrived the sun shone every day, making it the perfect holiday.

My life in Lilac Grove was spent in close proximity to that of my neighbours, the cramped back yards offering little privacy. The constant babble of children running in and out, combined with the frantic barking and whining from frustrated animals, at times made me long for solitude.

So I often recall that blissful afternoon when I went to buy a loaf of bread during our Norfolk Broads' holiday. Bill had taken the children to explore yet another windmill and Mother was resting from the heat in her cool cabin. Leaving the boat I found a narrow sandy path that led through an avenue of head high reeds. The ground was hot beneath my thin sandals and I was becoming dazzled by the brilliant light that flickered and flashed through the dark green of the reeds.

I moved slowly through this green tunnel, revelling in the heat, when suddenly the reeds parted and I found myself on the edge of a reed fringed lake. Half way across was the reason for my journey. A small waterside wooden shop that provided basic supplies for the holidaymaker. I continued with my slow pace, almost languid in my movements, unaware that I was becoming mesmerised by the complete silence, broken only by the soft whispering from the swaying reeds, during that soporific afternoon. Reaching my destination I entered the cool darkness of the shop, lit only by broad shafts of golden sunlight through shuttered windows and the open door.

I made my purchase, handing over the correct coinage. My half-whispered "Thank you" was greeted by a broad smile and cheerful nod. It was simply too hot for speech. Out into the burning heat I was startled by a loud plop caused by some water creature going about his business. I wondered dreamily whether it was Ratty or Mole. Reluctantly I retraced my steps knowing that each one led me further and further away from this mystical and enchanting lake. Back through the dark green tunnel and into cooler air than that from the sheltered lake, and I knew I was where I belonged.

The wonderful weather we had experienced during our holiday continued when we returned to Stockdale. At first it was enjoyable, and through the highways and byways people were greeting each other with happy smiles, but as the summer progressed and the temperatures rose, smiles turned to minor complaints. As time went on I began to find the heat in the avenue unbearable. There was no escape. The heat bounced off brick walls and concrete roads and pavements and I longed for the cool, green shade from the old willow tree in Grange Road. I spent as much time as I could with Mother, but the long walk there and back in the full heat of the sun in my condition was becoming too much.

Then, one hot day in June, Mother received news that James and family were coming to stay at Tearo House for a couple of days, en route to their holiday in Scotland. Although thrilled, Mother and I were uneasy and were soon to discover the reason why. James spoke first to my parents, and then I was told about the plan. James had come to plead the case of Aunt Emily, Father's younger spinster sister. James was very close to Emily and Grandma, as he had lodged with them while studying at his training college, and was saddened by Grandma's death some months before. He also knew that Emily was nervous about approaching her brother and sister-in-law with such a life changing proposition: She had a horror of living alone and hoped they could all live together in the large house in Surrey.

Father was overjoyed. Mother was horrified. I felt as if my whole world had collapsed around me. The thought of life without Mother was unbearable.

When James spoke to me his words were harsh and for a while I almost hated him. He told me I had to grow up and stop clinging to Mother, and that I should think about what she wanted out of life for a change.

I was distraught. But on reflection, I knew only too well how she longed to return to her roots.

However, Mother was feeling unsure about leaving Stockdale. Circumstances were changing. She now had a group of friends, was reinstated in her church and I was back in town with three grandchildren for her to love and nurture. But most of all her dream of an easy-care bungalow would very soon be fulfilled.

Eventually Emily and my parents reached a decision whereby they would shut down Tearo House and move to Surrey, but return when my baby was due and then reassess the situation. With a heavy heart I accepted the inevitable, but for a while, it seemed like a bad dream.

No Mother, no Tearo House. I was lost, but life has to go on and my wonderful friends were a great support. I had booked a midwife for a home birth and on examination she thought I may be carrying twins. The news sent shock waves through the two families, but on further examination she found the baby was lying in the wrong position. Bill's relief was overwhelming, but it was not such good news for me as I had to have the baby turned. Today this procedure is carried out in hospital under medical supervision but in 1959 it was a case of gritting my teeth, lying on my bed and hanging onto the headboard while my midwife, with one agonisingly, sickening twist of her strong arms, turned my baby.

The glorious summer continued and Mother and I wrote to each other every week, but the constant high temperatures, unbroken by cooling visits to Tearo House, were beginning to sap my energy. My baby was due at the end of August and Mother wrote saying they would return two weeks before my due date. I was overjoyed, as were the children, for they had missed my parents as much as I.

At last the time came and Bill contacted Mrs Bell's nephew for the key to Tearo House, for she had long gone and he was now the owner. The evening before my parents were due to arrive, we all went round to open up the house. Armed with brushes and dusters, we set about cleaning away spiders, cobwebs and dust.

Doors and windows were opened to let the soft evening air flow through the old house, bringing it back to life again. Beds were aired and we had brought food and coal for their first evening. The children ran through the house and garden laughing with excitement and pleasure to be back in the familiar home. Rather touchingly they had gathered an already wilting bunch of buttercups and daises with which to greet Nana and Grandpa. The heat was increasing and my clothes were beginning to stick to my skin as I carried on with my dusting, and I wondered whether there would be a storm. Bill had been wandering thoughtfully round the house, as if seeing it in a new light, and I wondered what was on his mind. Eventually I finished with the cleaning and lowered my swollen body carefully down in Mother's old armchair by the open window.

Listening to the happy laughter of Sam and Robbie, memories of other children's voices flooded over me and I was strongly aware of my parent's presence in that shabby old kitchen. I wondered miserably what would happen to the house if they did decide to move south. Ever since Mrs Bell died and left Tearo House to her nephew Frank, we had known that he was longing to carry out his plans to turn the house into two self-contained flats. Frank was not only a councillor, but a builder, so his plans did not present any problems to a man in his position. I recalled how month after month he would sit in this same kitchen with a cosy cup of tea and the hopeful question of, "Any signs of moving yet, Mr Ferguson?"

"Not yet, Mr Cooper, not yet," Father would chuckle. "We must just wait and see." These conversations always unnerved us even though we knew we were secure as sitting tenants, but we knew how desperate Mr Cooper was to claim what was rightly his.

Then suddenly, as if to echo my tearful thoughts, a storm erupted in a frenzy of thrashing trees, the clamour of deafening thunder and pouring, drenching rain. We watched from the safety of the kitchen, with Robbie squealing and laughing with excitement at the drama unfolding in the garden. Eventually the worst of the storm subsided and reluctantly we returned to the sticky heat of Lilac Grove.

It was so good to have Mother and Father back at the house and I spent as much time as I could just being with them. The heat continued and I counted the days to the end of August when my baby was due. August came and went, and by the ninth of September I was worried. I knew it was late for I was not likely to forget the date of conception.

But both the doctor and midwife dismissed my fears as that of an over tired pregnant woman. Finally my bouncing baby girl was born two weeks late and my midwife apologised for not listening to me, as she could clearly tell by the state of my baby's skin. It was dry and flaky to touch and she has had trouble with her skin ever since. Mother came to stay and took over the running of the household until I was able to cope with the children and animals. My wonderful neighbours called, one by one, to congratulate me and were royally entertained by Mother, who in turn, thoroughly enjoyed meeting all the girls I had talked of to her. Nurse Blackburn was the most unlikely looking midwife I had known. She was tall, aloof, and, I felt, would be happier presiding over a vicar's tea party rather than assisting with the most basic of human endeavour, birth.

She called each day to check the progress of both me and my baby, and on the second day Robbie wished to give his new sister a present. Nurse, baby and I were in the bedroom where I could hear him calling as he struggled up the long flight of stairs that led to the bedroom. "Mummy, just look at what I have got. It's a present for baby. I hope she likes it." His blue eyes were shining with eager anticipation at the pleasure baby would have in his wondrous gift. With a triumphant flourish he thrust out a chubby little hand holding by its tail a flea-ridden, decomposing dead rat. Nurse Blackburn gave a piercing scream and nearly dropped my precious baby. "Take it away, take that filthy thing away, you horrible little boy. Take it away this instant!" she screamed.

His eyes filled with tears and I longed to throw my arms around him for his impetuosity at wishing to greet his baby sister with, what was in his eyes, a special gift. Choking back my laughter and not wishing to incur Nurse Blackburn's wrath, as she obviously did not like little boys, I told him gently to go and show his gift to Nana, knowing only she would know how to placate a tearful little three-year-old boy.

The third day after I gave birth dawned cloudy, dark and it rained continuously, and the baby blues hit me like a sledgehammer. A huge black cloud of sheer terror and despair overwhelmed me and I cried.

How would I cope with three children and the animals? How much longer could I bear living in this house without a garden? How would I live without my beloved parents nearby, and if they really were to leave what would happen to the house? Would Mr Cooper claim his rightful legacy and finally carry out all those plans he had dreamt of for so many years, and would I ever see so much of my brothers if the house had gone? My mind whirled round and round in a frenzy of despairing possibilities and I sobbed and sobbed.

Chapter Twenty-eight

It was Christmas Eve 1959 and Sam could not sleep. I had celebrated her sixth birthday in November with the traditional bun fight, and although the party had been a success it had been chaotic enough to make me hesitate about repeating the occasion. Not wishing to disturb the sleeping Robbie, Sam and I crept into the spare bedroom hoping to catch a glimpse of Father Christmas on his yearly journey. A hard frost was steadily spreading over the rooftops as we gazed expectantly out of the window. I held her close, for by now she was shivering, not only with the cold, but with excitement. The cold night sky was alive with a myriad of twinkling, sparkling stars when suddenly I gasped involuntarily.

"Oh look Sam, there he is. It's Father Christmas. Can you see him. Look, look it really is him. Just look at all his reindeers." My over active imagination was out of control and I simply could not contain my excitement as this was the first and only time I had seen a shooting star. Nearly six years later Mother told me I really had to make Sam understand that Father Christmas did not exist; but after that magical evening Sam and I knew better. For we had seen him, had we not?

Surprisingly, after spending four years in Lilac Grove I remember very little of the Christmases we spent there. This seems to say a lot about the house, I feel. It seemed to be austere and unwelcoming in spite of my efforts to eradicate the gloomy atmosphere. It was so different to the cottage. Undoubtedly primitive though it was, its ancient and weathered beams and rugged stone walls created a highly distinctive atmosphere.

My parents went South for Christmas and, after many hours of long discussion with her brothers and Beth, now widowed, and much heartbreaking soul searching, they made the decision to finally leave the north. I was deeply shocked but not really surprised as I knew it was simply a case of 'Hobson's Choice'. It had been a mistake from the very beginning for these two people to move so far north. Life was so different during the 1930s and communities were not the cosmopolitan groups of today, and sadly north and south will never mix successfully. The happy Christmas my parents spent with Beth and her brothers made them realise that at their time of life the bond between siblings was as strong as that between children. When I knew my parents had made their choice, a sense of near panic overtook me and I felt lost and abandoned.

As the year turned and we were through the worst of the winter, my parents were to return to finalise the lease and make arrangements for the removal of their furniture. When I fully realised it was not only Mother I was losing but the house also, I was desperate. This just could not happen, something had to be done. There was only one solution, but could the impossible become the possible. I could think of nothing else. When I finally plucked up courage to approach Bill, amazingly he had been mulling over the same idea himself.

During the last twenty years Tearo House was beginning to show his age and was in need of loving care.

As Bill's father was a Master Builder, Bill had the knowledge and wherewithal to carry out the work, some of which would involve major alterations. This could prove to be rather daunting but I was prepared to meet any challenge; or so I thought. So Bill, with my parents, approached Mr Cooper, and after a great deal of legal wrangling, it was finally agreed that my parents would continue with the lease until Bill sold Lilac Grove. Emily, in her eagerness to have my parents with her, offered to pay the rental for this period.

I was delighted with this arrangement as it delayed their departure for a little longer. It took many months for the house to sell, but during this period Bill and my parents grew closer together and we became relatively happy companions. Bill did his best to make the last few months of their life in Stockdale as pleasant as possible and we went on many happy picnics on the wild moors that Mother so loved.

Finally, moving day arrived, and I left Lilac Grove forever. However, my departure was touched by a great deal of sadness at leaving my immediate neighbours and close friends, as their love and support had given me the strength that I needed during those troublesome years. Fortunately the distance between us did not affect our friendships which lasted for many months to come.

The day had been tiring and emotional and it was not until my excited children were finally settled in their new bedrooms that Bill took Father out for a celebratory drink. Father, in usual understated manner, was overjoyed at leaving the North East, but Mother was more thoughtful about their momentous decision.

After the men left, Mother and I sat together for the last time in the garden of Tearo House. We watched the soft evening light drift slowly into a perfumed purple dusk and I could smell the colour green all around me. The leaves of the huge old willow tree, the grassy lawns and the field beyond, all held their familiar smell and I could breathe again.

Suddenly Mother spoke and her words almost shocked me, "Well Mabs, I hope you are happy with what you have done." She looked thoughtfully up at the old house looming above us. "It needs a great deal of loving and I hope you fully realise what you have taken on." I began to feel like a spoilt child wanting more sweeties. Mother knew me only too well. As a family we never shared any physical contact between each other and certainly never used any of the empty euphemisms used so easily today. So I found it difficult when explaining to her, without sounding overly sentimental, that I loved her and that only Tearo House could fill the gap her absence would leave. We fell silent for a while after my faltering confession and by the end of the evening we both understood the strength of the love we had for each other.

Chapter Twenty-nine

The following day my parents had gone and there I was; mistress of Tearo House. Bill had gone to work, and while I busied myself with the children and unpacking, I began to assess my situation. I had stepped back in time, for in some ways not a great deal had changed.

The large farm behind the church, and to the north of Grange Road, had been swallowed up by a pleasantly landscaped council estate, and the big fields beyond the beck at the bottom of the garden had suffered the same fate. Many of the residents of Grange Road remained the same, with relatively few changes. At the other end of the road, and to the south, the bakery still flourished. It was now run by the two sisters as their parents had retired. Happily the red telephone box remained by the Institute, thereby enabling me to ring Mother whenever I had the money to pay for the call.

Surprisingly, my adjoining neighbours at No. 21 were still the same family and their presence strengthened my longing for continuity as so much had recently changed in my life. Mr Prosser was a retired music teacher, and as a child I had hidden behind the high hedge in the front garden and listened enthralled to the wonderful music. During the warmer weather windows would be opened and I would thrill to the full power of his magnificent grand piano. This has led to a lifelong love of classical piano music. The Prosser's had one daughter who drifted aimlessly through life searching for her Romeo. Eventually her search ended and the hapless man came to live with his inlaws at No. 21.

Mother, with a very naughty twinkle in her eye, would laughingly remark to Father how tired the poor boy was looking!

My other neighbours were a Mr and Mrs Johnson who, with their two children, Sylvia and Harry, had moved in during the summer of 1946. They replaced the quiet and gentle Mrs Davies, who had so kindly let us use her air raid shelter during those terrible years of war. The Johnsons proved to be quite a shock to my parents, as they were larger than life and so very different to most of the residents in Grange Road. This volatile family made no pretence at hiding their physical and vocal shouting matches. Mother and I were regularly entertained by the sight of Mrs Johnson throwing an assortment of her husband's belongings out of the back bedroom window and into the garden below, while screaming hell and damnation at the wretched man. The children also were highly skilled in this verbal art making. Father muttered irritably under his breath at the use of such language.

Mrs Johnson was a highly skilled dressmaker, and as Mother greatly admired her skill, a strange kind of 'over the garden wall' relationship grew between the two women.

Samantha and Robbie were to begin their schooling in September at the same school that Mark and I had attended, and I would walk with them four times a day along the same road, still unchanged with its fields and allotments.

Nothing much had changed. Even Mr Watson's two sons delivered the coal into the scullery as had their father all those years ago. The dreaded scullery did not appear quite as frightening after my experiencing similar conditions in the cottage and Lilac Grove. However, Bill found it completely unacceptable and was constantly making plans to improve the situation.

So much needed improving that it took Bill several weeks to decide where our priorities lay. With the advent of television our lifestyle had changed, from spending our leisure time round the kitchen table and listening to the radio, to sitting upstairs in the large draughty living room around the small television set. The huge Victorian fireplace seemed to be designed to send the heat up the chimney instead of heating the room, so Bill arranged with his father that one of his men would fit a new and modern fireplace as long as Bill removed the old one. This was all well and good, until one evening Bill arrived home armed with a huge sledgehammer and a couple of grimy dust sheets.

I stared in sheer disbelief as Bill took one almighty swing at the solid slate mantelshelf. He left me no time to cover the floor or furniture, or even remove ornaments and curtains, before he was hammering at the slate surround like a man possessed. I watched horrified as the twenty-year-old wallpaper began to split and tear across the wall while brick dust and soot filled the shabby room. I helped Bill carry out the pieces of slate into a quiet corner of the front garden, as they were so heavy he could not manage on his own. While waiting for the new fireplace the children and I spent our evenings round the kitchen table and listened to the radio. This arrangement did not inconvenience Bill in any way, as he spent every evening at the local pub.

The modern tiled fireplace was finally installed. The dingy wallpaper was stripped and in true DIY fervour Bill took down the old picture rail and replaced it with an attractive Delph rack. The cracked walls were replastered and a professional decorator papered and painted the large room. I was overjoyed. Fortunately my delight and gratitude blinded me to the threadbare carpet and mixture of furniture from my parents and Bill's old home. As always, the curtains were home-made, but these huge windows would have proved a challenge even to a professional dressmaker. Snowy white net curtains helped to dress the window and overall the general effect was not displeasing. A small window in the left alcove overlooking the garden was also difficult to dress. The transformation to this elegant and gracious room took several weeks, and in the meantime I was still coping with the scullery and the large steps into the kitchen. This room remained untouched and as a family we ate at the same table I had known as a child. My housework routine was much the same as Mother's had been, apart from two coal fires to clean out and light each day. This was a time-consuming chore as the ashes had to be carried outside and halfway around the house to the dustbin.

Since moving to Tearo House I had not seen anything of Jilly and Frank. They too had had a recent house move and were also busy with decorating, but Frank had kept in touch with Bill at the garage. So I was highly delighted when, one summer's day, Frank came knocking at the back door. The children had just left for school after their lunch and I was busy in the kitchen. Frank settled down comfortably in Father's old chair and I made the traditional cup of tea. We chatted and laughed for a while, but I

93

was longing to show him my newly decorated living room and quite unconsciously used the terminology that was used in Tearo House. Giving him my most beguiling smile, I said, "Shall we go upstairs now, Frank?"

His mouth dropped opened and his rimless spectacles misted over alarmingly. "What did you just say, Martha?" He choked out in red faced embarrassment.

For a moment I was confused by his reaction, then realised how my offer would sound to a stranger to Tearo House. My pink faced embarrassment matched Frank's as I duly led him upstairs from the kitchen, through the hall and into the living room. Our friendship with Jilly and Frank continued and we still visited each other's homes, but our riotous evening parties slowly dwindled as Jilly became pregnant. Sadly, by the time their son was nearly school age, Frank died very suddenly, and for some reason or another I lost touch with Jilly.

My friendships from Lilac Grove lasted for over three or four years and we continued with our monthly get togethers at each other's homes. With the passing of time we began to stretch our wings and leave the barriers of domesticity behind to take up paid employment. This led to very different lives, but I did keep in touch with one close friend.

Chapter Thirty

Bill's success with the living room drove him on to attack the huge problem that was the scullery. This had been one of Mrs Bell's doubtful improvements and was clearly a mistake. A mistake my poor mother had to endure for over twenty years, I might add. (There was one other 'improvement' of which, as yet, I have not spoken and that is the bathroom. This room, like the playroom, was used for many different functions and only added to the quirkiness of Tearo House.) But back to the scullery. In order to incorporate a fridge, a plumbed in washing machine and a gas cooker, into the narrow kitchen, there was only one solution and that was to extend from the south facing wall. Luckily, Bill had his father's best architect, bricklayers, carpenters electricians and plumbers to carry out the work. The original sash window and door were replaced by a level floor and brick wall, together with a large square bay window. This window was large enough to contain a fridge, sink unit and washing machine. The gas cooker stood between the new window and door, which had been moved into the corner of the room. The open coal fire was replaced by a coke burning stove and the right alcove was finally bricked up.

Flooring tiles were laid over the old stone floor, with a large colourful rug at the fireplace. An old sideboard and two heavy wooden carver chairs, by courtesy of Annie, appeared and, along with Mother's wooden kitchen table covered by a checked tablecloth, the room had a slightly rustic look. All this work took many months of intense disruption and upheaval, and sadly the garden became a casualty from all the disturbance and began to look like a builder's yard. As I recall those dreadful days, I wonder how I coped with three small children and excitable animals to look after. I took it all in my stride and was only too happy about the alterations.

Then, on one autumnal day, a gypsy came knocking at the front door. This was a yearly occurrence as Stockdale was surrounded by small villages that held the rites to hold country fairs and sell horses. Gypsies from far and wide gathered at these fairs and the women folk would come into the town to sell their wares. Mother, in spite of her religious beliefs, was strangely superstitious and would always 'cross their palms with silver' but I was going to make a fresh start. I listened to the whining preamble that always accompanied these transactions, took a deep breathe, and politely refused to buy her clothes pegs.

Now, this particular woman was much older than most and was pure Romany. From her weather-worn features and dark wary eyes, to her jangling earrings and copious shawls, she was typical of her race. At my refusal to buy from her she seemed to lose all control and began to curse me with all the venom and hate she instinctively felt for none Romany people. Her grimy skirts swirled around her scrawny body as she shook her fist at me with fury, while cursing me and my children and my children's children. Her parting shot was to curse me and my home and all who should live there, in true Romany fashion. As a child I was used to Mother coping with these people, but had never heard an outburst such as this, and in spite of my bravado it unnerved me for quite some days to come.

I slowly adjusted to my new life in Tearo House, and was never happier than when baking all sorts of goodies for the children on their return from school in the afternoon. I delighted in the large airy room overlooking the old willow tree, and as a family we ate two meals a day round the old table. I wrote glowing letters to Mother, on a regular basis, about my wonderful new kitchen and how much easier it was to care for the house now that the scullery no longer existed. Even though we had a sunny, comfortable living room with television upstairs, the children and I seemed to linger in the kitchen and garden until it was bath time.

Inspired by his success with the alteration to the kitchen, Bill was eager to begin his next project. For quite some time he had felt that the Victorian porch darkened the hall, so once again, armed with his heavy hammer, he enjoyed dismantling the inner door and wall. The heavy outer door was replaced by a wooden door with strengthened glass panes, which indeed lightened the dark hall, but after twenty years of having the security of two doors I felt a little exposed to the world. The smart new door now led on to the modernisation of the hall, landings and staircases. The enormity of this project meant that only a professional decorator with sufficient scaffolding could complete the work.

For the next few weeks I had to squeeze around the scaffolding while watching the Lincruster paper and Dado rail being removed, and the cracked walls replastered and then papered with the very popular woodchip paper. Everything was then painted in a warm cream paint and the transformation was truly surprising. We still had Mother's old stair and hall carpet but I happily accepted that these things would eventually be replaced.

It was now Christmas 1962 and I could not contain my excitement. I always enjoyed this time of year. Most mothers of young children do, I imagine, but this year was different. Mother was coming to stay for a week and I was overwhelmed with joy. Not only did I long for her to see all the changes we had made, but it meant that she would watch the children opening their stockings on Christmas morning with me in the bathroom.

The bathroom? I hear you cry! So now is the time to describe the part the bathroom played in our lives.

When my parents rented the house in 1937, Mrs Bell had made two major alterations to the house: The scullery and the bathroom.

The bathroom and the fourth bedroom were on the first floor, with the other three bedrooms on the second floor, forming a large square landing. The fourth bedroom was converted into the bathroom and the original bathroom was a spare room. It was known as the box room, as it contained Father's old army trunk and various other cases and chests, and as time went by our bric-a-brac was added to what my parents had left.

The bathroom was a large pleasant room with a small fireplace into which had been fitted a gas fire. Attached to the gas fire was a single gas ring on a stand.

A large chest of drawers and a small wooden chair furnished the room, with a mirror over the fireplace and a shaving mirror

e

for Father over the basin. The sash window overlooked the farms, fields and stream and was my favourite view from the house.

When my parents moved north, Mother found it difficult to acclimatise to the colder weather and, as she was the first to rise in the mornings, she would begin her day in the bathroom. A tray with a small teapot, cup and saucer and milk jug, was carried up three flights of stairs the night before. She would light the gas fire and boil the small kettle on the gas ring for her first cup of tea. The gentle hissing and plopping sounds, together with the instant warmth from the tiny gas fire, would slowly coax my mother into facing yet another gruelling day in the icy scullery. And so it was that this cosy room became the place in which to prepare oneself for either cold downstairs rooms or equally cold upstairs rooms. Therefore it was not surprising that on Christmas Day mornings, we children, clutching our stockings, would head for the bathroom where Mother would be waiting with a cup of tea and biscuits.

Naturally I continued the tradition with my children, and this year was so special as Mother was sharing our happiness.

Chapter Thirty-one

During the years I lived at Tearo House with my parents the bathroom was to witness many dramatic events, but one particular situation, concerning a girl, comes to mind. Her name was Olive, and Mother met her at the hairdressing salon where Olive worked. She was a hauntingly beautiful girl and lived with her mother and sister in a smaller house nearby. Her mother was Irish and widowed and there was an elder brother who proved to be as elusive as Olive.

Olive would quite often disappear. She supposedly spent time in London, then returned a few weeks later to continue her life in Stockdale. On her return she would bring a small memento of London for Mother, and in order to thank her properly Mother would invite her in for a cup of tea. I was a teenager at that time and beginning to take an interest in the fashion trend that was sweeping the country. It was a reaction to the austerity of the war years, and Olive followed the new look assiduously. During her visits I would sit in the corner by the fire as she chatted gaily to Mother and carefully absorb every detail of this beautiful girl. She was my idol! Aware of my gaze, she would cross and uncross her long, slim legs so as to display her elegant court shoes to their best advantage. Her frothy white petticoats would crackle seductively beneath her full skirts that flowed from a small waist. Her dazzling smile displayed perfect teeth and her chatter was gay and highly amusing, but there was a troubled look to her large brown eyes.

As the friendship deepened, Mother was able to confide in Olive how difficult it was to pay hair care for both me and herself.

Olive generously offered to care for our hair at home for a small fee, and so our hilarious evenings in the bathroom began. After all the shampooing and curling and crimping and preening was completed, we would sip cups of tea and munch biscuits while revealing all sorts of womanly secrets to each other. One evening, not long after Christmas, an opened bottle of sherry from Uncle Don's hamper was brought out and a very merry time was had in that strange old bathroom.

By the time my relationship with Bill was common knowledge, Olive had disappeared and none of Mother's contacts knew of her whereabouts. However, one day, when I was pregnant with Samantha, she appeared with the usual small gift for Mother. Sensing something was wrong, Mother invited her in and slowly a sorry tale of broken hearts was revealed. We did our best to console her and eventually there were tearful smiles, but we felt there was an underlying sorrow she could not disclose. Nothing more was heard of her for many years, until one glorious spring morning not long after Bill and I had moved to Grange Road.

I had taken the children to school and instead of returning to the housework I continued with my walk. It was a perfect day and I was glad to be alive. The alterations in the house were going well and the old place was filled with the laughter of young life, and I was happy. I then realised my walk had taken me to the road where Olive's mother still lived. The gardens were small and neat with low hedges and doors, and windows opened to the sun. As I approached Olive's old home I saw something in the front garden. A low rumbling, groaning, grunting sound was coming from beneath many shawls and rugs wrapped around a hunched body, while two outstretched skeletal arms seemed to be waving to me. Olive's mother appeared at the doorway and, on seeing what the noise was about, greeted me with, "Good morning, Martha. Beautiful day," in her usual clipped Irish accent, then turned back to the house. By now the person in the chair was becoming agitated, and unsure as to what to do I smiled a polite hello. The person jerked and grunted at the sound of my voice, then icy cold horror washed over me as I found myself drowning in the pain and agony and despair in those beautiful brown eyes. Our gaze held for what seemed an eternity, until I finally whispered a tearful "Good bye, Olive," and stumbled my way back to the familiarity and security of Tearo House.

Slowly, through the weeks and months to follow, the shabby rooms were papered and painted. Floor covering and curtains were to be obtained when there was sufficient money to pay for these items. My third child Lucy, a delicious bundle of chattering feminine charm, was still at home with me. I was deeply involved with Sam and Robbie's school work. As money was always short I was still wearing hand-me-downs from friends and family while trying to keep abreast with clothes for the children. I shopped for and cooked two hot meals a day for Bill and the children as well as baking small treats for when school had finished.

As previously mentioned, although the house had improved, the garden had suffered and become the dumping ground for all the debris from the house. I made several attempts to improve the damage but it had lost its former glory. I continued to mow the lawns and weed the beds, but as Bill had removed a couple of trees the magic had gone.

I kept in touch with my friends from Lilac Grove and we spent an occasional entertaining evening with Jilly and Frank. Rather endearingly, as mentioned already, Frank took to calling in at odd times when his business brought him to the area. The old house seemed to attract him and he took an interest in the alterations.

My brushes and paints had been packed away long ago but I never gave up my reading. I had always read avidly, as did my family, and in spite of my busy life always found time to read. I discovered Howard Spring during the 1950s, and devoured all that I could find of his work while wondering why I felt such a deep empathy with this particular author. One day, when visiting my parents in the south, I was at a family get-together. While Mother was happily reminiscing with her siblings, Howard Spring's name was mentioned.

I was amazed to find that Grandpa Frazer taught a group of aspiring young authors the skills of popular writing and that Howard Spring had been an outstanding pupil. I realised I had instinctively sensed a bond between the two men and now understood my feeling of recognition. Surprisingly, Mother was rather blasé about my amazing discovery, and happily continued with her family to name-drop some very well known people of that time.

Bill had enjoyed his part in the redecorating of the old house and I could see he was itching to use his hammer again, although nothing was said of what he had in mind.

101

I usually enjoyed a leisurely visit to the library at the weekend with the children, just as Father had done when we were small. However, this particular afternoon, Bill offered to look after the children for a change. Although surprised by his offer, I gladly took the opportunity to enjoy the library on my own. I was pleased with my choice of books for myself and the children and looked forward to discussing them with Sam and Robbie.

On my return, I opened my new front door with a happy smile, and was confronted by clouds of billowing sooty brick dust swirling around the hall and staircase reaching up to the bathroom landing. I began to cough with the choking brick dust, and tears of fury and despair were very close. He had done it again. No discussion. No thought as to what I may or may not want.

Robbie ran down the stairs, stumbling through the rubble, squealing with excitement and laughter, his hands and face covered in grimy dust. "Come and look, Mummy. Come and look at what we have done. Just come and look at all the mess." Sam, always the quiet one, hovered anxiously nearby.

I hesitated as I stared unbelievingly at the utter chaos Bill had created. Robbie's excitement began to fade as he sensed my mood.

"Dad says it will look good when it's all cleared away. I'll help you to clean up, Mummy," his voice trailed away uncertainly as he was near to tears. I looked down at their little faces, and controlling my anger did my best to reassure them that I was only a little bit cross. I always did my best to hide any rows that may occur between Bill and myself so I carried on with the usual routine of supper, bath time and bedtime.

Although the old bathroom made the landing rather dark it was a useful space for storage, so when Bill demolished the two sturdy inner walls without emptying the room I was a little surprised.

The debris was ankle deep and it took nearly two weeks before the plastering and painting of this corner could be completed. A new window replaced the old frosted one and now the garden and fields could be clearly seen. I made new curtains and rescued an occasional table from our bedroom that Mother had left behind, polished it until it shone, then placed a jug of colourful artificial flowers on its gleaming surface. It went well with a large Victorian chest of drawers that mother had also left in the old bathroom. It was now a bright and sunny interesting corner which added to the quirkiness of the dear old house.

When it was finally finished, I had to admit it had been a good idea of Bill's.

Looking back at those frantic years, I think they were the happiest times in our somewhat turbulent marriage. This family of three small children, one rabbit, one hamster, one budgerigar, three cats, two dogs and a goldfish in a bowl that time and time again provided a tasty morsel for the cat, tumbled around in this awkward house in daily confusion, and in spite of Bill's inadequacy I still loved him.

Chapter Thirty-two

But storm clouds were gathering. Not only in Tearo House but with my parents in Tadworth. We had enjoyed a happy holiday with them at the big house, where Robbie had teased poor Emily mercilessly, there were visits to Hampton Court, the Tower of London and Uncle Jamie's bungalow with a garden that ran down to the River Thames. There was a landing stage where a small rowing boat was tied firmly to its moorings. It was pure Wind in the Willows.

Sadly, the relationship between Father and Emily was becoming rather fractious and Mother was caught between the bickering siblings. Father was a difficult man, there was no doubt. He was well educated, intelligent and a perfectionist but he was dogmatic and stubborn. He loved Emily but there was one unspoken problem between them, and that was money. My grandparents had been very wealthy people and, although I will never know the truth, I can only surmise that when Father came back from France, badly wounded and mentally damaged, Grandpa spent a great deal of money in restoring his son's health. When my grandparents died, Emily inherited what Father felt was rightly his.

Not only did Emily inherit her Mother's estate but also property belonging to their maternal aunt. Aunt Margaret, another independent, wealthy spinster, died leaving Emily a large three bedroomed bungalow, crammed full with priceless antiques. The bungalow was situated on the South Downs, along the coast road between Brighton and New Haven, and as tensions between

Father and Emily were rising it was felt the bungalow was the only solution. Once again, Mother was uprooted from her home and had to begin another life all over again. She soon settled down to new routines and was genuinely welcomed into the small local church. Even Father, although not participating in the services, became involved with small church activities. We were lucky enough to spend the most perfect of holidays with my parents for the next seven or eight years.

During the 1950s and 1960s changes, politically and socially, were taking place. I watched, on a 12 inch television set, Roger Bannister become the first man to run the four minute mile. I thrilled to Virginia McKenna's heartbreaking Juliet and listened to the commentary as Yuri Gagarin became the first man in space.

None of these events touched my life, except to marvel at the stupendous achievements, until Stockdale opened its first night club. Bill began to talk about this wonderful new form of entertainment and then one day arrived home with a large bag of new expensive clothing. Shirts, jackets and trousers were all displayed to me while explaining that one had to be smartly dressed to go to these places. There was no mention of taking me and I was left to simmer with controlled fury and frustration, but eventually had to accept the situation.

Bill began to attend the night club regularly, and rather worryingly would arrive home at odd times during the evening, until late one night Jilly and Frank knocked at the door. I was surprised and pleased to see them, until they tried to explain the reason for their visit. Like most business people in Stockdale they had visited the night club and had seen Bill there. It was obvious they were finding it difficult to warn me that Bill's evenings were not as innocent as I believed. I tried to explain that I trusted Bill completely and hoped that he would never knowingly hurt me. These dear people could not understand my absolute trust in Bill as they were only concerned for my welfare.

After they left I had much to dwell upon but said nothing of their visit to Bill. I simply watched and waited, sensing something might happen.

Then one summer morning I was to be told by Bill something that changed my life forever.

I was at the kitchen sink preparing our midday lunch, when Bill came home early. He had perched on the kitchen table behind me and I carried on with my work, not realising something was wrong.

When he spoke, his voice was quiet and strained and my whole world stopped as I listened to what he had to say.

Bill was forty-two years old, a very heavy smoker and drank every day. He had been working too hard at the garage, and together with the high life he was leading, had contracted a severe heart defect. He was to stop work immediately and take two weeks bed rest with strong medication. He had also to change his lifestyle.

We stared at each other, trying to understand the implications of the diagnosis. Bill was in shock and I found it difficult to think coherently.

How would I live without this man I loved so completely? How would I survive as a widow with three children. I longed desperately for him to hold me close and reassure me, but as usual my advances were rejected and I had to cope with my fears and worries alone.

Bill was a difficult patient, but slowly with my loving care his confidence returned as his health improved. He began to take charge at the garage once again, but the business was heading for trouble. I was frantic with worry at the strain he was under and nightmare memories of Father's unemployment returned to haunt me; I simply had to find a way to earn a little extra money.

I contacted my friends and within a week had two mother's-in-law, two mothers and one friend who had recently become employed, all wanting me to clean their homes. By the end of the first week I had earned the princely sum of £5.00. This was the same amount Bill had given me as housekeeping allowance.

I chose my time to hand over the precious money, and the moment came when we were all at the dinner table. I held out the envelope containing the money to Bill and he hesitated. The children looked at us, from one to the other, sensing the tension as Bill told me very quietly that as I had earned the money I could keep it, but he would not be paying me any more housekeeping. The children, not understanding the situation, cheered at Dad's generosity. And so began my life of heartache and drudgery. I had taken on this work with the genuine desire to help Bill with his money problems but he seemed to resent my burst of independence, which I found very upsetting.

At first I quite enjoyed the work; meeting new people and different surroundings. Sam and Robbie were at school, and as Lucy was only four years old I had to take her with me, but fortunately my ladies did not object. She was an adorable child and settled into the routine quite happily. She never complained at the long boring hours she spent with me or the many, many miles we walked in all weathers. This we did to save on the bus fare. I was at home in time to make a lunch for Sam and Robbie, but Bill's hours at the garage were becoming more unreliable. He began to come home during the afternoon, complaining of tiredness and taking to his bed, but was always well enough to sup at his local hostelry during the evening. Money matters were never discussed; so as not to worry me, he said, but I sensed the business was in serious trouble. I continued with my cleaning round but Lucy was to begin school that September so, in order to be with her for the first few weeks, I changed my hours.

Lucy adapted to her new life at school very well as she had her brother and sister to look after her. Yes, there were tears at the beginning, but they were my hidden tears as the last of my fledglings left the nest of babyhood. I had treasured every moment of those five years and adored each child, so different in character and temperament. However, I soon became happily involved with all the exciting preparations for Christmas that were taking place at their school. I tried to ignore my fears for the business, so was completely unprepared for the shock that was to come.

Winter came early that year. Snow, wind and freezing rain bringing the usual worries as to whether Bill could pay for the essential coal delivery. As history repeats itself, I too waited anxiously for my letter from James containing a cheque as a Christmas gift.

A week before Christmas the postman handed me a bundle of rain smudged cards and letters. As I opened a badly smudged letter and read the contents, my legs gave way beneath me. I read over and over again those incomprehensible words. 'The occupants of Tearo House will be evicted on 31st December.' It was as if the horrors of my childhood were happening all over again.

I confronted Bill as soon as he returned, but was harangued for opening a letter addressed to him. He eventually calmed down

107

and explained I should not have seen the letter as the problem had been solved. It was an uneasy Christmas but I was greatly cheered by spending a day with Mark, Prue and their baby son.

However, a month later Bill approached me 'cap in hand', as it were, to ask whether he could sell our only sofa. This item had belonged to Aunt Barbara and added a touch of class to the living room and I was very unhappy about its departure, but as Bill, in turn, was to sacrifice his expensive fishing rods, I had to agree.

Later on, when an oak hall stand, a much loved wedding gift to Mother, and an antique chair which I coveted, had to go, I felt our marriage was beginning to show the cracks.

Chapter Thirty-three

The weeks flew by as there was so much to be done. My cleaning round, the children's schooling, the house and garden, and never ending knitting and sewing for our clothing. I was beginning to feel tired, bone crushingly tired, and the only thing that kept me going was the time we spent with my parents at Telscombe Cliffs.

Our holidays at the bungalow were, quite simply, idyllic. Somehow Bill managed to scrape together enough money to pay for the petrol, the AA route map and money for Mother for our keep.

As there were no motorways in those days, Bill needed time to familiarise himself with the long journey. As I was the map reader, I too needed to acquaint myself with the route. As already referred to, the bungalow belonged to my great aunt, who bequeathed it, complete with antique furniture, to my Aunt Emily, who in turn let it to my parents for a 'peppercorn rent'.

The bungalow was spacious enough to be mistaken for a house, with a garden the size of two tennis courts. It was set on the edge of Telscombe Tye overlooking the sea. The most extraordinary effect Telscombe had on us was the quality of light. It emanates from the chalk on which Brighton and area is built and was an intoxicating cocktail of energising brilliant light and sweet pure air.

How Mother coped as we all piled out of the car to invade her peace and quiet I will never know. She took everything in her usual calm manner, even when on at least two occasions we turned up with an extra child; friends of Sam and Lucy. When

Mark and Prue with their baby came down too, she would shop, cook and make up beds for nine people. With very little practical help from us, I might add. At one awkward time we even took a little dog that we could not leave behind, who almost immediately gave birth to four pups. Bill had to drown three of them but we kept one puppy for the bitch.

Mother was a premature baby weighing only five pounds at birth in December 1899. Granny kept her alive by swaddling the infant in thick cotton wool in a sturdy shoebox in the oven. This was kept at room temperature until the baby gained weight. Mother suffered from undiagnosed angina for as long as I can remember and I can only suppose her tenacity and resilience came from her strong Christian belief.

As neither my parents or Bill had money to spare, our pleasures were of the simple kind. Picnics on the beach, flying Robbie's kites high up on Cuckmere Haven or morning coffee in the converted railway carriage at Hove. But the real magic of Telscombe was being with Mother. She had the rare gift of making the most mundane occasions an exciting adventure. Sitting round the huge oak dining table in the sunny dining room, having breakfast, would invariably turn into gales of laughter from Mother's quick wit.

Playing card games during the evening, while Bill and Father were enjoying there nightly drink, the children would choke with laughter as Mother cheated so outrageously, the ash of the cigarette she was pretending to smoke growing longer and longer. Rainy days, which were rare, would be spent climbing into the huge loft where Father would give us the family history of each precious item. The exquisite large doll's house that Grandpa had made was a magnet to Sam, Lucy and myself. These magical holidays would end all too soon and the long drive home was inevitably rather sombre.

The girls were doing well at school. Sam had taken the Scholarship and was to attend my old Grammar School. Lucy was turning out to be the bright one in the family. When enquiring about her progress I asked if I could help with her reading in any way. I was told she was like a sponge, absorbing knowledge for the sheer love of learning and was a joy to teach. Academically she should have been in the class above but was forced by law to remain where she was. They had to work hard to prevent her becoming bored and I had to provide a calm home background. I did my best to keep the tensions between Bill and myself from her but it was not always easy.

Sam was different. She was outgoing, confident and in many ways another version of myself. At the beginning of her second term I was very surprised when she told me that she had had an audition with her music teacher on the piano and that she was to have piano lessons at school. None of this made sense as we had never had a piano and I could not understand how Sam showed such promise. Her teacher wrote to me explaining that she had a 'natural ear', which is very important in playing an instrument, and that she instinctively played each correct note. She was very excited by Sam's ability and foresaw great things for her.

So now it was essential that we had a piano on which she could practise. I was thrilled to know my little girl was so gifted and was determined to find a piano.

Bill was pleased with her achievement but sadly the cost of a piano was beyond his means. I was desperate; how on earth could I afford a piano? It was out of the question, so in desperation I rang my friend in Lilac Grove. Not for one moment did I think she would be able to help, but unbelievably, after she had rung round her friends, she found that Pam wanted to get rid of an old upright piano. I could not believe my luck! Not only did she have a piano for sale but her husband was prepared to bring it over to Tearo House, and all for the small sum of ten shillings.

And so the playroom became the music room. Tearo House began to sing again and we all joined in with the fun on the piano. Chopsticks being the one and only rendition we were capable of until Sam began to play properly. A friend of Sam's who had had private tuition helped Sam and it was pure joy to hear the two little girls playing together with such skill. Sam's lessons at school were only half an hour a week but she forged ahead with her exams until finally graduating at grade eight. It was plain to see that music was in her blood. I would hear her leave her bed, patter barefoot downstairs to the piano, and then play with such powerful emotion until she was drained of all her energy. It would be the same when returning from school, the same burst of emotional outpouring that was not satisfied until she had played every last chord. I would sit with her, simply listening, while she played her scales and practice pieces, marvelling at this golden haired gifted child of mine.

Then there was Rob. My dimpled, mischievous, impetuous, auburn haired son. Within the family group he was energetic, hot headed, and always involved in some prank or other. Then, to my horror, I realised he was being bullied at school. My fury at such cowardly behaviour was overwhelming and I was on the point of seeing his headmaster, but Robbie persuaded me not to do so as it would make matters worse.

I began to watch out for him under the pretext of collecting Lucy from school. Bill taught him one or two boxing moves which gave him a little more confidence. One day Rob took a hard swipe at his persecutor and knocked him out. After that the bullying ceased and that shy and timid little boy grew into the man he is today. In most families it is plain to see which is the favourite child but I loved my three children equally. Each one so very different. It would be impossible to love one more than the other.

Chapter Thirty-four

It became increasingly clear that Bill was bored with the garage business. He grumbled that the work was too heavy for him and that he was tired. He complained that the responsibility of paying two men's wages was a heavy burden, and began to spend more time at home. In all fairness he did look rather weary and I worried about his heart condition. He began to talk about paid employment, to let someone else pay his wage. Eventually the business was closed down, the machinery sold, the men paid off and the property returned to his father's ownership. I suspected by now that his father's generosity had finally dried up and that Bill was having to fend for himself.

He attended one or two interviews for various positions with little success, then one promising position was advertised and I was almost delirious with excitement and hope. The interview was arranged, and dressed in his best bib and tucker I waved him off, praying with all my heart there would be good news. Two hours later the front door slammed in such a way to tell me he had been drinking and my heart sank. I was told in highly colourful language "that he was damned well not going to be told by any spotty faced youth how to do his job" and then he walked out.

The shock of his childish behaviour was so great I was physically sick, and I feel it was from this point I began to seriously consider whether my genuine and sincere love for this difficult man was faltering. I was angry without a doubt and, although I sympathised, I was beginning to harden toward him. He would have to claim unemployment benefit, and my cleaning money was important, but I was desperately worried as to how we were going to manage. It was the nightmare of my childhood happening all over again and I wondered whether I could cope as well as Mother. There were signs of decay all around. The garden was unrecognisable, its cool beauty lost forever, and the freshly painted house was showing signs of wear. But when Bill pinned an old blanket where the double doors had been in the wooden garage I felt we had reached the point of no return.

As an innocent and so naïve seventeen-year-old girl I was blithely unaware of the serious predicament I was in when becoming pregnant by a married man. Bill panicked and tried to abort my pregnancy but when it failed he knew he was trapped. Mother was well aware of the danger I was in, for this was the 1950s, and breathed a sigh of relief when we finally married. Mother never knew of the attempted abortion, I was too ashamed, and there was always an element of gratitude in my love for Bill. However, now, when I found I was pregnant for the fourth time, I was terrified.

I was thirty-two years old with three small children. We were living on a shoestring and I would not be able to carry on with the heavy cleaning work. Tearo House was a large and expensive property to maintain and it was looking shabby and neglected. I kept remembering the two other occasions when Bill had tried to abort my pregnancies and was shocked and miserable at his eagerness to abort me yet again. However, this time was different. My marriage was unstable and the future uncertain. I was emotionally and physically exhausted and was having trouble in thinking rationally. The year was 1967 and fortunately abortion had finally been made legal.

Worn down by Bill's insistence, I reluctantly gave in and went to see my family doctor. He was sympathetic to my problem and an abortion was arranged. It was a serious operation and as something went wrong I was rather ill. Mother came north, as I was hospitalised for over a week, leaving Father in the capable hands of Aunt Emily. She looked after me and the children for over two weeks, and with her wisdom, love and understanding of the situation I was saved from suffering a complete breakdown.

In the meantime Bill's father had died and Bill was talking about starting another business. He befriended a man who promised great things. And once again I was uneasy about the proposed future.

Dick was a manager with a large nation wide building company and promised all the work that Bill could cope with. He was to lay kitchen and bathroom flooring tiles in all the new build houses. Bill took a training course and, armed with all the correct qualifications, set to work. I had given up my cleaning round and hated having to almost beg for money from Bill, but one day my local shopkeeper, knowing roughly of my background, told me that another customer had said her husband was looking for a receptionist in his new photographic studio based in town.

I plucked up all my courage and gave him a ring. I then went for an interview and he offered me four afternoons a week with a good rate of pay.

Bill was working odd hours, and as Sam was nearly fourteen and a very capable young lady I knew the children were in safe hands. I waited excitedly until we were all at the dinner table and told them of my good news.

"Do you mean that some man is actually going to pay you real money to work for him?" blurted out Rob unbelievingly.

We all laughed and the girls congratulated me. Bill was noncommittal.

It had been fifteen years since I was last employed, so I was a nervous wreck when my first day arrived. However, I soon settled down, and was thrilled to receive my first pay packet. Once again I waited until we were all seated at the table and proudly handed my unopened packet to Bill. He looked at it for a moment, then with a voice of utter contempt said, "I am not taking another man's money. Here, you keep it." And with that he threw it across the table, and left the room. The children were frightened by the anger in his voice and I did my best to reassure them, but something died inside me that evening. I felt we were losing whatever we had had between us for so many years.

So began my working life, which lasted until my seventieth year. I was to have a variety of varied positions. Some very well paid, most a good average rate, and all with an artistic trend. But I will tell more about them as I continue. I was soon promoted to a five day week at the studio and life took on a hectic and erratic routine. Bill was working odd hours as the nature of his work so dictated. The laying of floors usually had to be done when all other services had been completed. As my work was nearby in town, I came home at lunch time to feed my hungry children and then see them off to afternoon school. During the day Bill was going in and out to various meetings and discussions about mysterious matters. I was home for the evening meal and bedtime as Bill would be leaving for work.

There was no such thing as childcare in the 1960s and I was determined that my children would not be known as 'latch key kids' which was often the case with others. It was heavy going from the very beginning. As Mother predicted, Tearo House was challenging, particularly with the eternal battle against cat and dog hairs as well as all the other mess that they create. I was also still coping with a coal fire in the living room. This particular chore in the old house was definitely a case of 'upstairs and downstairs' with me playing the scullery maid. The work was time consuming, and involved a great deal of running up and down stairs. Because of the shabby exterior, I made sure my huge windows sparkled inside and out, that my net curtains were always snowy white and the paintwork, although peeling, was clean. Fortunately I was young and enthusiastic, and enjoyed the freedom from Bill's controlling attitude toward me, even though his erratic moods were still frightening.

Meanwhile my children were growing up. Robbie, the scamp, was showing a strong desire to make money. He wanted money and was prepared to go to any lengths to achieve his aim, by fair means or foul, I might add. He took on a paper round. Then he enrolled as a choir boy at the local church and was available for weddings and funerals. He took his responsibilities very seriously and seemed to enjoy the music, but I think it was the companionship of the other boys that appealed to him, as it had been so sadly lacking at school. However, unknown to me or Bill, he had a nice little scam going with one of his friends. They stole empty glass bottles from the back of a nearby off-licence then, with their prepuberty innocent faces, had the nerve to return them and claim the rebate. Quite a few weeks later they were caught red-handed by the owner who frightened the life out of them with talk of policemen and prison.

Bill was highly amused by his illegal activities and found it difficult to be angry with his blue eyed son. I realised I would have to keep a close eye on this bundle of aspiring young masculinity.

116

Christmas was growing near and Robbie told us he was to sing solo at the highly popular carol service that year. The girls and I found it hard to believe and teased him by asking him to sing for us, but he refused, muttering under his breath about nosey women.

The evening grew close and I began to worry. Supposing his nerve gave way at the last moment and he could not go through with the ordeal. He would be destroyed if this was to happen.

The moment came. The organ began to play and I clasped Sam and Lucy's hands on either side of me. Rob stood up and I gasped. Could this really be Robbie. This red headed, freckled faced, angelic urchin in a neck ruff? He took a deep breath then began to sing. His voice soared round the old church as pure and sweet and melodious as any trained chorister. Tears of pride, astonishment and relief trickled down my cheeks, while Sam and Lucy were open mouthed as their brother completed the carol. The atmosphere was electric and I saw one or two elderly ladies wipe away a tear.

It was a moment I will never forget, but sadly there was a worrying and disturbing end to his singing career. Time passed, then one evening in late summer Mr Smith, the choirmaster, came to call. He understood that we had a piano at home, and as Robbie's voice showed great promise he wished to give him private tuition in his own home free of charge. I was very impressed by his request and readily agreed to one hour a week. Robbie was rather hesitant at first but it soon became the norm for Robbie to have his singing lesson each week. However, I was slightly puzzled by Robbie's irritability when the lesson was over but said nothing. Then one evening, on my return home from work, Bill had given the children their meal and was waiting in the kitchen. He passed me an open envelope saying, "What are you going to do about this?" His voice was angrily accusing.

I read the handwritten letter addressed to Robbie three times before the full horror sank in. "But this is a love letter, Bill, to Robbie from Mr Smith. What does it mean?"

Perversion of this nature was completely unknown to me at that time and I did not know how to react, but Bill was more able about the seedy side of life and told me that Mr Smith was never to come to the house again and that Robbie should leave the choir immediately.

When Mr Smith turned up for the weekly lesson I told him that Robbie would be leaving the choir and that he was not welcome to my house.

Robbie was rather quiet for quite a while, as he had so enjoyed the friendship of the other boys, but youth is resilient and he was soon involved in other pranks with his friend Jeff.

Meanwhile, another shock was waiting for me in the shape of Mr Wilson, Lucy's headmaster. He wanted to see me about Lucy's progress at school and what he had to tell me has haunted me all my life. He began by asking whether my marriage was breaking down. I instantly denied that there was any trouble at home. I could sense he was irritated by my denial and told me she was showing the classic symptoms of a child from a broken home. To prove it he showed me her books from year one, and I was horrified by the steady deterioration. Tears were very close as he explained that his teachers were trained to handle a distressed child but they were sorry to see this happening to such a promising pupil.

I have carried the guilt of what Bill and I had done to our so precious child for the rest of my life. I had always done my best to present a happy marriage to my children, and for most of the time we were a close family group, but I had to admit there were failings on both sides.

Chapter Thirty-five

Sam had completed her scholastic career relatively smoothly and had been outstanding in her music. She sailed through her Grade 8 exam and gained the admiration of her music teacher but, as so often happens, she had befriended a girl who thought all classical music was a bore. Theresa was a confident girl who at times displayed a streak of arrogance. She came from a large extended family where uncles, aunts and cousins were often to be found at the home of her widowed mother.

This close family group attracted Sam, as we never had the local connection. Bill kept us away from his family and mine were southern based. The two girls became very close and were constantly in each other's homes. Sadly, Sam's interest in music waned, partly because of Theresa's influence. I had looked into the cost of private tuition but found the fee to be prohibitive. During Sam's last year at school all the girls were taken on a three day sightseeing trip to London. Sam and Theresa thoroughly enjoyed the experience as it opened their eyes to another world. A world I was not to know about until much later.

By this time I had become rather bored with the narrow routine between myself, Mr Munro and one other girl, so one day I quite impetuously rang the studio that had treated me so cruelly when I worked there previously. By now the old man had retired and his son and daughter were running the business. An interview was arranged and, with legs feeling as if they were made of rubber, I entered the familiar building. There had been some changes, but basically it was still the same. I talked with Mr Henry, trying to appear confident and mature, but failed completely. In spite of my embarrassment he offered me a position.

I now had more money in my pocket and was able to contribute a little extra to the housekeeping. Bill's business was unreliable and he was having to take work wherever it was offered. This meant erratic and unsociable hours, but between us we always managed to be there for the children.

The summer of Sam's school trip proved to be interesting in that I had to accept that she was growing up. She told me that she and Theresa had met two Persian boys when they had visited London with the school, and that the four of them were corresponding with each other. These boys were supposedly from very wealthy families and were studying at a university in London.

By now Sam and Theresa were studying for an in-depth business course at the local college, I was working full time in the next town and Rob was helping his Father at the weekends with floor laying. During the summer holidays that year, because of Bill's and my working commitments, we sent Sam, Lucy and Theresa on the train to King's Cross, where they were met by my parents and escorted to Telscombe Cliffs. Bill, Robbie and I drove down later. On my arrival at the bungalow Mother told me of her surprise when two smartly dressed and very polite young men turned up on her doorstep asking for Sam and Theresa.

Mother being Mother invited them in and questioned all four as to how they had met. Then she probed into the boys' backgrounds, and when she was relatively satisfied agreed to the boys taking Sam and Theresa out and about until we arrived. She enjoyed their long chat and almost believed that Sam's boy was the son of a prince. I was rather concerned about the way the relationship was growing but hoped it would prove to be her first holiday romance. As always we had a glorious holiday filled with love, laughter, sunshine and fresh air. Luckily we were not to know this would be the last year we spent with Mother.

The boys continued to write and I could see Sam was becoming rather thoughtful. Then one day, when they turned up at Tearo House uninvited, Bill's temper snapped and he told them in highly colourful language to leave his daughter alone. Luckily Sam seemed to recover from the affair quite well and soon became her normal happy, laughing self.

As so often happens when one is gainfully employed, other more lucrative opportunities arise. And this was how I became Supervisor of the Reprographic Department in British Steel Research. The work at Mr Henry's studio was interesting and satisfying, and I was on good terms with the rest of the staff, but three years later, when this opportunity came my way, it was too good to refuse. So it was with a heavy heart I left all that was familiar and entered an unknown and challenging future.

Holly was five foot nothing, buxom and with blue black hair. She was the Addressograph Multilith Operator and together with Mr Davies we made a department of three. As Barry was the company's photographer his work took him out a great deal and it was my job to take over during his absence. This involved operating a Process Camera which was used in the production of graphic material and was rather daunting at first.

After a few months Barry was moved to pastures new, leaving me in sole charge of the department. Holly was fourteen years younger than myself and had celebrated her twenty-first birthday not long before I met her. As a young girl she had experienced shocking domestic brutality from a drunken stepfather but was now happily married with a baby son. Her husband was a trainee architect and they were struggling to buy their small town house. We worked together for four frantic years, sharing each other's triumphs and disappointments.

The intimacy of our working relationship merged into our private lives and the bond that grew between us is as strong now as it was then. However, there was one occasion when our maternal instincts overrode all male authority during our working time. Holly's little boy had mumps and the nursery refused to care for him. Holly was frantic, as women were not paid if they took time off to nurse sick children, so there was only one course of action we could take. The plan was so audacious and serious that if we were caught it meant instant dismissal. We worked in the basement of a large Victorian building. The room was huge, with a very big table on which to sort out our work etc., and underneath we kept boxes and boxes of paper, and chemical materials. We devised a kind of cave whereby the child could hide. Somehow Holly managed to smuggle her little boy past the prying eyes of the doorkeeper each day and then we tucked him up in his special cave. We spent the entire nerve-racking week

121

f

trembling with fear every time someone came in, praying that Gary would neither sneeze nor cough. Incredibly we were not caught, but looking back it was the most reckless and foolhardy action to undertake simply for a week's wages.

Inevitably my children were growing up. By now Lucy was attending the same Grammar School that Sam and I had done and it was strange to see her wearing the same uniform.

Sam had left the early teenage period during which she lost a great deal of weight. I lovingly knitted a beautiful thick woollen dress for her, mistakenly thinking it would help to disguise her painfully thin body. To my horror it turned her into Olive Oil, Popeye's No. 1. The wretched garment clung to every curve of her body, making her look thinner than ever. Fortunately, she joined in with the laughter her stick insect looking body provoked but begged me not to have to wear the awful dress. Before long this skinny waif blossomed into a long-legged, willowy golden haired beauty with an infectious giggle and a twinkle in her eyes.

Robbie was still at school but was showing little promise in any particular direction. He willingly helped his father with any flooring work at the weekends, but even these were becoming more infrequent. Then one day Bill took Rob out for a day's fishing, or so I thought; for when they returned my whole world turned upside down. Bill had signed Robbie up for six years' service in the Royal Navy. I was so shocked I could not immediately take in the enormity of what Bill had done.

Yet again, no talk or discussion, but this time he was playing with people's lives.

Bill had controlled me all my life, but this time he had gone too far and was playing with the life of my child. Waves of horror washed over me as I tried to absorb the details of what they had done. As I listened to Robbie's bubbling, childlike enthusiasm about his exciting future, I knew I had to smile and offer my congratulations while controlling my fury for Bill's thoughtless action. Robbie was not yet sixteen, small for his age and immature, but somehow Bill had managed to sign the boy up in a watertight contract without Robbie fully understanding quite what had happened.

I spent many hours on the phone to Mother, until she was able to help me realise it was all for the best. But I could never forgive Bill for what he had done.

While all this was happening, Theresa was coping with the terrible loss of her mother. She was the youngest of three children, with a married older sister who was to be her guardian until she was of age. Her sister and new husband were planning on building a small annex to their house for Theresa but the alterations were to take at least another year. Jill tentatively enquired as to whether Bill and I would be prepared to take her into our home for that period.

Bill was strangely amenable at first, until the evening came to discuss the financial situation. We were seated in the playroom, comfortably chatting, with tea and biscuits to hand, when I sensed Bill's mood was changing. When Jill asked him directly whether or not the arrangements were satisfactory, he simply walked out, saying to me, "You do what you want. It's all up to you, so please yourself." There was a stunned silence and Sam looked near to tears but I was able to reassure Jill that there was no need to worry. It was a heavy responsibility to take on the care and welfare of a seventeen-year-old girl but my heart went out to her.

In some small way she helped to fill the gap that Robbie's absence had created, and at first it was all quite fun. I enjoyed sharing in their young lives at college and all the excitement at their preparations for a night out together. Eleven-year-old Lucy watched them quietly from a distance and I had to make sure she did not feel left out. After his outburst, even Bill enjoyed the teenage silliness they brought to the old house.

Following a miserable first few days at the beginning of his Royal Navy career, Robbie began to settle down and was soon able to come home for frequent short leaves, usually bringing friends with him.

Chapter Thirty-six

One bitterly cold morning in February 1972, Mother went into the garden to feed the birds. Still wearing her dressing gown and slippers, she slipped on the frosty lawn and broke her ankle. She lay there for nearly half an hour, but as Father had damaged ear drums it was a long time before he heard her calling. Aunt Emily rang to say Mother was in hospital and I immediately made arrangements to take the long journey south. Mother was her usual cheerful and positive self, but she looked tired. She was in pain, as her ankle had been rebroken and set again.

I made the most of my short time with her in hospital before my journey back to Stockdale, promising to return as soon as work permitted. I kept in touch by phone until the day of that fateful phone call to say Mother had died of a heart attack on March the 7th.

Bill and I travelled down by night coach to the funeral and I sobbed quietly all through that long dark journey. Robbie had requested leave for his grandmother's funeral and he sobbed as much as me. She was buried high on the hilltop cemetery in the beautiful village of Telscombe. This was a favourite walk of ours over the years, every summer. It was good to see my brothers and family but I was still in shock. Poor Father had looked completely bewildered all through that awful period and James felt Father would be happier with me in Stockdale. Back at Tearo House I took his cup of cocoa to bed one night and found him sitting with his head in his hands. "It was different on the firing line," he said.

I sensed something dreadful was coming. "How was that, Dad?" I asked gently.

"Well, Lassie, you didn't know who had the bullet."

I realised with horror that my gentle father had had to shoot point blank some poor wretch blindfolded and tied to a stake. I also realised he blamed himself for Mother's death. He was with me for a couple of months, then stayed with his brother John for a while, and then back to Aunt Emily in Surrey. Meanwhile, James had found a place for him in a home on the south coast. I found the thought of Father in a home abhorrent and made enquiries with the Social Services about having him with me, but I was advised against this idea. And so I began to take regular trips to visit him in the home at Seaford. I would leave work Friday, travel through the night, arrive Saturday morning then leave Sunday evening.

Six months later I was rushed into the Isolation Hospital where I remained for two weeks, but against medical advice I signed myself out at the end of the second week. Bill and I had had yet another row the night before I was taken ill and I could not bear the tension that lay between us while I was in hospital. Also there were changes in management at work and I suspected they would affect my position. When I saw my doctor I was told I was one hundred per cent toxic and I was in isolation to protect me against more infection as I had been desperately ill. However, I did recover, and life with Bill quietened down once more. But the girls needed me as well. The death of their beloved Nana had upset them as much as Robbie.

Sam and Theresa were in the middle of their final exams at college, but Sam was feeling guilty about my having to pay all her expenses, clothes and pocket money. Her guilt was accentuated by Theresa's ability to spend money whenever it was needed.

We also had another addition to the family. Two years previously Lucy had had a few riding lessons from a friend of a friend of Bill's, and always longed for a pony. This had seemed to be an impossible dream until one day Bill, in his usual inimitable manner, arrived home after a drunken encounter with a gypsy, with a pony. This was all well and good, but neither Bill nor I knew how to care for the animal.

Pip was a bay gelding 13.2 high and had a wall eye. He was unkempt, forlorn and unwanted, and for Lucy and I it was love at first sight. However, a pony was a great responsibility and we had nowhere to keep him.

Unknown to me, Lucy spent the whole of that first night with him under the willow tree and he was there for the next few days. Eventually, Lucy found a field some distance away from Grange Road where he stayed until we arranged with old Mr Robinson to keep him in one of his stables for a small rent. Lucy took on two paper rounds to pay for this expense and I paid for his feed, hay and straw. Slowly Lucy and I became familiar with him and he was the most adorable animal I had known. And his obvious love for Lucy was touching to watch. He would stand on the other side of the fence snorting and neighing to attract her attention and when she appeared his excitement was quite obvious. She soon broke him, as he was a docile animal, and groomed and cared for him until his shaggy coat was restored to its full glorious chestnut colour. Lucy had to ride him with only a cloth saddle to begin with, as the price of a leather saddle was beyond either Bill's or my pocket, but after a year Bill bought the coveted leather saddle for her birthday. I had bought her hat not long after she had Pip as this was essential for her safety. Living nearby was a friend of Lucy's who also had a pony and the two little girls rode the highways and byways happily together. Quite how far they roamed I was not to know until only recently, I might add!

By now I was becoming used to Robbie turning up at odd times with one or two friends, all in various stages of inebriation. Chaos, confusion and laughter would ensue until they left as suddenly as they had arrived, and we girls would return to our equally confused way of living.

Finally, Sam and Theresa had both finished their studies at college and had both found employment.

Theresa had a clerical position at a local solicitor's office and Sam was running her uncle's architect's office. Bill's brother was a well known architect in Stockdale and was in partnership with two other friends. Sam had proved to be so efficient at her work that Ronnie almost loved her as much as his own daughters.

Theresa had been given money for driving lessons, and Sam did her best to hide her envy, but neither she nor I could possibly afford such extravagance at that time. Theresa also had a boyfriend. An aspiring and promising young footballer. Theresa was rather smug about the relationship, particularly when he turned up at Tearo House in his gleaming new car. But Sam, too, was conducting her own love affair in the shape of romantic letter writing. She had been communicating all summer with a contemporary of Robbie's from HMS *Drake*. Ironically, his name too was Bill and we were about to see him on our television screen. The boy had been chosen as part of a team who were to perform a daring sword display at the Royal Albert Hall on Remembrance Night. We were all there, the girls, Bill and myself, with bated breath. Suddenly Sam squealed, "That's him, that's him." We gazed intently at this handsome young man and I knew with all the certainty of my feminine intuition that she would marry the boy. After the performance he travelled north as soon as he could and Sam was truly in love. During that long summer he visited us often, when his leaves permitted, and eventually a date was set for the wedding.

There had been drastic changes at British Steel and my life was changing. Holly was pregnant and due to leave within the month. There was talk of a man overriding my position, and when I requested time off for Samantha's wedding I was told politely but firmly not to return.

Chapter Thirty-seven

I had only six weeks in which to arrange a church wedding with fifty guests. This was due to the groom having to go to sea with HMS *Kent* for several months, leaving just before Christmas. The time had finally come when Bill and I had to put aside all our grievances and work together as a team for the sake of our daughter. After much discussion we both agreed even the most humble of receptions was beyond our means and decided that a sumptuous buffet to be held at Tearo House was the answer. Once a plan had been agreed upon we set about our allotted tasks.

With the help of his sister, Bill arranged trestle tables and white tablecloths to be laid out in the sitting room. A table holding the two tiered wedding cake, which I had paid for, was to stand in the bay window and the other tables held the buffet. Bill paid for most of the food, which was to be half a salmon, half a fresh ham and two local cheeses as the main course, and on the day Bill and I completed all the trimmings until the table was groaning with delicious fresh food. Bill organised the drinks, which were to include champagne. I booked the church and the reading of the bans, the photographer and the flowers. I organised accommodation for all the people who were travelling up from the south and somehow managed to find time to buy a dress and a hat, with a rather unfortunate feather, for myself.

Theresa was the main bridesmaid, with Lucy and Bill's younger sister. Theresa had finally left my loving care, quite happily I suspect, and was now living with her sister in the next village. Because of the age gap and the distance between us, it proved difficult to come to a final decision, but eventually a particular style was agreed and the dresses were purchased. However, time was running out.

While, as I thought, I was still happily employed by BSC, the girls and I set out to purchase the wedding dress. As I was working on a tight budget it required careful consideration but miraculously we found it on the same day. Another stroke of luck was the price. Apparently it was classed as shop-soiled, but the stain on the bottom of the train was so small it would never be seen and it was marked down to less than half price. It was a classic Empire Line design made of rich satin and guipure lace. This beautiful heavy lace fitted firmly under her bust, covering her neck and shoulders and finishing in a romantic hood as the headdress. The train, in heavy satin, fell from just below the shoulders in smooth uncluttered folds ending in a rounded hem. From the elbow to the wrist the satin completed the sleeve.

Another cost-saving touch of magic was the fur hand muff I made for her. I bought the materials from the local market and arranged with the florist to attach a delicate spray on to the muff on the morning of the wedding. As she was a winter bride the whole effect was quite perfect.

A week before the wedding I had an appointment with the bank manager during my lunch time to arrange a small overdraft. I had never spoken to such a revered personage before and was distinctly nervous. However, the evening before, when Lucy had gone to the stables to groom and feed Pip, she noticed a difference in his behaviour. He was restless and agitated, and as the evening wore on it became obvious that the dreaded condition of colic had taken hold of the animal. The vet was called out and he administered a colonic drench and instructed us to keep the animal on his feet at all times until the spasms cleared. This required a great deal of manpower as we had to keep him walking to prevent him from going down and rolling on his tummy to relieve the agonising pain. All through that cold dark night in November, Lucy's friends, Bill and I pushed and pulled, supported and encouraged the poor creature as we walked him up and down, hour after hour, in that long field.

As evening turned into night, Lucy's willing friends had to return to their homes and it was only Bill's cheerful cockney chatter that kept us going. Midnight came and went, and on and on we walked. The caring vet called again and the prognosis was more positive. The spasms were easing and the worst was over. By 3.00 pm Bill and I left an exhausted fourteen-year-old Lucy in the stable with her beloved animal. She reassured me she would be all right and reluctantly I left her and crawled into my own bed.

The next morning, after a couple of hours' sleep, I hurriedly threw on the coat I had worn the night before and left for work. All too soon it was my lunch break and nervously I entered the bank. I was ushered into the inner sanctum and as Mr Lovejoy took my outstretched hand he gave me a quizzical look. Glancing down at my leather coat I realised it was covered in dried mud from the activities of the night before. I stumbled my way through an embarrassing explanation of the terrible happenings to my daughter's pony. Happily, after some considerable thought and much questioning, he granted my request.

The evening before the wedding Sam spent with me and I sensed something was troubling her. Bill, Robbie and friends were all celebrating a bachelor night out and Bill was in his element. The sitting room looked positively bridal with its snowy white tablecloths and the wedding cake standing proudly on its plinth in the gracious bay window. In order to detract from the shabby curtains and carpets I had filled the house with flowers. Vases, jugs and containers of all description were to be seen on every shelf and every corner that could hold a vase. When my task was completed I was pleased to find the overall effect enhanced the bridal atmosphere.

My brothers, with their children, uncles and aunts, who had made the long journey north, were resting in their respective hotels as were Bill's family and friends. Everything was ready. Lucy, who was not a bridesmaid type of person and was feeling nervous about her part in the day's proceedings, had gone to bed early.

Sam and I were sitting quietly together with our own thoughts in the playroom. She pulled a cushion from the sofa and came to sit on the floor beside me. There was a long expectant silence, and after taking a deep breath she whispered, "Mother, I am pregnant."

Instantly before my inner eye there flashed an image of an infant girl with a mop of black hair. I hesitated, shocked beyond belief. How had I not seen? How had I not even noticed all those little telltale signs of pregnancy? She was so young, so vulnerable, I wanted to throw my arms around her and protect her from all that she would now have to experience. Instead I told her quietly and firmly that she did not have to go through with the marriage because of her condition and that I was quite prepared to cancel everything to protect my child from an unhappy marriage.

She burst into tears and told me she thought I would be angry at her misdemeanour. I held her close and told her that of course I was not angry, but that she had to be absolutely certain that she wanted to marry Bill. With shining eyes she told me how much she loved him and yes, she wanted to marry him. And who was I to doubt such teenage ardour.

Chapter Thirty-eight

The day of the wedding dawned dry and frosty with a strong winter sunshine. As the church was at the end of the road there was no confusion over finding Tearo House for the reception.

There was a gasp of admiration from the congregation when Sam entered the church on Bill's arm. Her dress, with a cosy hood and hand muff, looked so right for that sparkling cold day.

The ceremony was soon over and when everybody had collected at Tearo House the celebrations began. The wine flowed, telegrams were read, speeches were said and food was consumed with great gusto. The younger guests fell into small comfortable groups in the kitchen, playroom, stairs and bathroom landing while the older element rested in the sitting room. The house was filled with laughter, gaiety and happiness and I could almost feel him smiling as he hosted the wedding of the baby girl that had been born there just nineteen years ago. The young ones seemed unwilling to break up such a good party and the night was very dark before the last merry guest left, leaving Bill and myself to begin to clear up some of the debris while talking the day through.

Some days later, Holly and her husband Harvey, knowing of my anxiety about the shabby house, called to thank me for such a good party. They explained that the air of casual formality mixed with an easy atmosphere was due mainly to the quirky house. He added, with a twinkle in his eye, that the sight of mine and the girls' panties hanging on the ceiling rack was very homely.

Holly and I worked happily together for nearly five years in the basement for the British Steel Research Department. We took an immense pride in our work and were congratulated several times on the quality of the printed matter we produced. So it had been a great shock when I was told, so abruptly, to leave. However, through a business contact of Holly's, I had been offered another position with Brackenborough Borough Council. Initially, I had been undecided as to whether I should accept this new position, but after the rather brutal dismissal, I jumped at the offer. I was to work in the Art and Design Room with a young man called Geoff.

Geoff was a bit younger than myself and lived with his parents. Although he was quite experienced in the work we were doing he often made very silly mistakes and I had to keep my eye on him in case of any backlash. The work we did fed the machine room and the finishing room so we were kept rather busy. It was all so different to my time with Holly.

In the meantime, Sam was to continue working for her uncle and was booked into Stockdale's hospital to have her baby. Bill was still at sea and proving to be a rather hysterical father to be. Fortunately, Sam was able to cope with his moods in spite of the distance between them.

Lucy was now at senior school and enjoyed the first two years, but unknown to me was very unhappy during the latter part of her schooling. All this came to light while discussing my writing with her and caused me to wonder quite how much damage we working mothers inflict on our children. Her unhappiness was caused by a sadistic male teacher who did his utmost to break the spirit of my lively daughter. I was deeply saddened to realise she had coped with this adult bullying all on her own, but thankfully I have seen the same stoicism and endearing sense of humour that was in Mother.

Robbie was still coming home on leave and helping Bill with any small flooring jobs at the weekends. I could see Robbie was growing very close to his father and I was concerned about the values and attitudes Robbie was absorbing from Bill. I was also aware of an unspoken distance growing between Robbie and myself, and was not too sure as to how to handle the situation.

Slowly, the long awaited signs of spring began to appear and with it came the time for my first grandchild to be born. Sam's labour began late Friday night and she was admitted to hospital on Saturday afternoon. Robbie was home on leave and, with Bill, came to see her, but as her labour was increasing both men found it difficult to watch. I sat with her and we talked and laughed about everything and nothing. Hour after hour it went on as I rubbed her back and held her tight when the pains were strong, but I could see she was tiring badly. It was approaching midnight and I was becoming worried, but the nurses seemed to be unconcerned. I was becoming anxious. Something was wrong. As I was about to scream for attention, a worried nurse whisked Sam off to the delivery room. Suddenly I was capped and gowned and taken into the delivery room too, where I was told they had been watching us together and Sam was so exhausted she was not reacting to their instructions. As I was the only person she understood I then became the interpreter. By now her condition had deteriorated and the doctor was called in. Using what looked like a large ear trumpet he listened to Sam's tummy and then I heard those terrifying words, "The foetal heart has stopped." Suddenly a cacophony of sound whirled around me. Clattering feet on tiled floors, voices harsh with urgency and fear, horrible whooshing sounds and Sam screaming. I watched, numb with exhaustion and bewilderment, and abruptly a squirming bundle was thrust into my arms.

"There you are, Grandma. You hold him." I was told by a voice tired with strain.

I stared down at the wrinkled face and all I could think was, "You nearly killed Sam. You nearly killed my child."

Sam was very ill for a long time, as part of the afterbirth had been left inside her and it became infected. We were told it had been a serious double forceps birth and that Sam might not have any more children, and as it happened she did not.

I took quite some time to recover from the shock of watching the birth of my grandson. I was slightly unbalanced, detached from normal behaviour and found it difficult to concentrate on my work in the art room.

My son-in-law was not to see his son until two months later when he returned from sea. Apparently, as the story goes, he was drunk for nearly a week while at sea celebrating the birth of his son. This did not go down very well with Sam, but Robbie was duly impressed as was Bill! It was the summer of 1974 and the weather had been particularly pleasant. I was forty years old and my heart was breaking all over again. Sam, with her husband and baby, were to leave Stockdale and begin a new life in married quarters in Portsmouth.

I knew I was fortunate to have had her with me for so long and that it was inevitable that at some time or other she would spread her wings, but I have had to learn the hard way to say goodbye to all those I held most dear. However, there was still Lucy, Pip, Bill, Tearo House and a full time job to keep me busy.

Bill's so-called flooring business, that was supposedly to make our fortune, never quite took off. It slowly drifted into occasional lucrative contracts which became less and less as time passed. Where the money came from I was never to know but there was always enough for his cars, clothes and nights out.

Granted there had been some small improvements since the initial redecorating of the house, but peeling paintwork and blocked gutters did not seem to worry Bill too much. I had to learn to live with two brick pillars bereft of their caps which supported a rusty iron gate, supplied by courtesy of his father years ago.

Sadly Sam had become very homesick and begged us to stay with them for a while. I was concerned and, as Bill was between jobs, Lucy and I took time from school and work so we could all drive down to Portsmouth.

The flat was surprisingly roomy, with wonderful views from a large kitchen window looking up over rolling hills. The stone staircase and landings, however, were none too pleasant when the lift was out of action, which was more often than not, and then Sam had the problem of a baby in a pram and shopping to carry to the flat.

We had a happy time with them and at one point Sam, Lucy and myself had one of our giggling fits. This often happened at home, but this occasion was caused by an innocent remark made by my son-in-law over a particular naval tradition of which he was very proud. Sam immediately saw the funny side, then Lucy and I could not control ourselves. The two men glared at us, and their obvious bewilderment at the cause of our laughter only served to increase our hysterical giggling. Eventually we dried our tears and gained control of our senses and happily our outburst seemed to relax the tension I sensed in Sam.

We finished the week with a day trip to the Isle of Wight on the hovercraft, but all too soon it was time to leave Portsmouth. The sadness of our departure was softened by the promise of a return visit to Stockdale for Christmas. Hopefully Robbie would be on leave as well, and I was overjoyed at the thought at having all my family at Tearo House for the festivities.

Chapter Thirty-nine

To lessen the pain of separation, Sam and I kept in touch by letter, writing in much the same way as Mother and I had done. There were letters to Father as well, trying to keep his spirits up. Sadly he was not settling in the home James had found for him and I knew he was very unhappy. There was talk of him staying with his sister for Christmas, but after that my brothers and I would have to think again.

Before long I found myself beginning to prepare for Christmas. Lucy had by now left school and was looking for work but we were finding it difficult to find a suitable position for her. It was a worrying time, as she seemed so lonely now that her brother and sister had left home. Fortunately, she had Pip to care for and exercise, but she needed the mental stimulation of companionship. Bill did his best to look after her, as I was at work all day, but I could see the lethargy of unemployment was beginning to affect her. But Christmas was coming and she was a great help for me in preparing beds for our visitors. It was heavy work in those days, with thick blankets and bedspreads, as I had been unable to invest in the latest innovation of bed making called the duvet.

During the festive season Tearo House would wake from his summer slumber in order to protect us from the winter storms that invariably hit the north east coast. His sturdy brick walls and strong wooden supports would creak and groan as they retracted with the drop in temperature, and I new he was ready for another winter.

It was Christmas Eve, and my family had arrived the day before, safe and sound. They had all gone out to make an early start to the celebrations, leaving Lucy and myself to look after my baby grandson, which I did quite happily I might add. Coal fires were burning, the building was warm and inviting and the shabby old house was all dressed up in his Christmas finery. Tearo House loved Christmas.

Lucy had attended a job interview during the week and had been called back for a second interview that very morning. So when the phone rang at 7 pm to say she had been accepted as a trainee pharmacist's assistant at the local pharmacy we were overjoyed. We hugged each other, almost in tears with relief and nearly speechless with excitement. As you can imagine, we could not wait to tell the family our wonderful news.

It was a happy, boisterous and drunken Christmas and all too soon Bill and Robbie had to return to barracks. However, Bill was to begin another sea trip with HMS *Kent* and was to be away for another three months. It was decided that Sam and her baby would continue to live at Grange Road while they saved up for a place of their own in Stockdale. Now that Lucy was working, I felt it would be a help for me with the house and garden as well as my full-time work.

Sam told me she had been very lonely in Portsmouth even though she was with Bill as he spent long days at the base. Shortage of money prevented them from socialising and, as they were struggling with Bill's small wage, tensions were growing between them. I was hoping that the long break might help to improve their relationship.

Meanwhile, as all this was going on at home, Robbie's innocent young life was becoming a living nightmare. Whenever he came home on leave he had seemed quite happy about his career and there was no sign of the misery he was experiencing. Whether Bill suspected anything I will never know. Then one spine-chilling day Bill received a phone call from Robbie's Superior Officer to say that Robbie was officially missing without trace. This was considered to be an offence punishable by imprisonment and if he contacted us in any way we had to let the authorities know immediately.

Apparently he had completely disappeared, wearing only the clothes on his back and leaving behind all formal identification.

Bill and I were shocked to the core. Almost incapable of logical speech or coherent thought. We became two separate entities hardly able to speak to each other, isolated in our own particular misery and unable to offer comfort in any shape or form. Pain, despair and anger, bordering on sheer fury, at the cause of Robbie's torment coursed through my veins. The mind numbing lack of information was slowly gnawing away at my sanity, while my whole being was crying out in pain to hold my child safely in my arms.

Hour after hour, day after day and week after week, dragged on and on. I became zombie-like in my speech and actions, so much so that one day, while at work, a young girl from the machine room discussing a printing problem, asked carefully whether there was anything wrong. I was surprised and deeply touched by her concern and told her about my son. It was some small relief to know that somebody in the work place knew of my situation. How I longed to have Holly by my side as she had been when Mother had died. Her instinctive ability to care for people, her down to earth approach to life, mixed with a crazy sense of humour, was what I needed to keep me functioning on an even keel. But as this could not be, my borderline insanity was urging me to pray that his body would soon be found. Certain death would be preferable to this uncertainty.

Chapter Forty

It was Lucy's day off and my two girls were alone in the house with Sam's baby. I was at work and Bill was somewhere on business, when suddenly there was an urgent knocking at the back door. Startled, Sam opened the door to an exhausted Robbie.

He was dishevelled, unshaven and his thick red hair had grown unusually long. He was strained and edgy and in no mood for polite chat. Sam instinctively knew how to handle her young brother and immediately gave him some food and a hot drink. There was only enough time for him to eat when there was a thunderous knocking at the front door by the police. Lucy quickly saw Robbie over the garden fence and away across the fields as Sam delayed opening the door, complaining that they had woken her sleeping child. She was told they knew Robbie was there and they proceeded to search the house. To no avail, of course!

The girls were questioned rather harshly and Lucy recalls that when asked directly if she knew where he was, she replied, quite truthfully but defiantly, that she did not know where he was and even if she did she would not tell them! She was severely reprimanded for her rudeness, but there was a twinkle in the eye of the policeman who obviously admired the loyalty between siblings.

On my return home from work I was told about everything that had happened, and that Bill had had a phone call to say the civil police now had Robbie in their custody and we could see him for a brief time before the naval police arrived. My state of mind by that time was, understandably, near breaking point. The overwhelming relief that he was alive was almost too much to bear, but fortunately I did so.

Bill and I waited in a stark bare room at the police station where Robbie was brought to us. He had been fed and cleaned up but, as was the rule, his trouser belt and shoe laces had been removed in order to prevent him from making another escape. Watching him shuffle awkwardly towards us, clutching his trousers round his thin body, was a sight I will never ever forget. With a brave attempt at a watery smile he greeted me with his usual cheery manner, "Hello Mother, how's things?" It was almost too much to bear.

When we returned from the police station to tell the girls what had happened to Rob, Bill as always left me alone and went to the pub. After he had gone I had never felt so desolate, despairing and, in a strange way, betrayed. Why had he left me? On that day of all days, when I had so desperately needed comforting and to share our grief together, Bill had been incapable of showing any tenderness or affection.

The girls and I chatted quietly together about everything and nothing as there was too much to say. That would all have to come later. Much later. The police told Bill that they hated handling these cases as it usually meant one thing, and these boys were not criminals in their eyes, although they had to be treated as such.

Rob spent the night in a police cell waiting collection by the naval police to be taken to Portsmouth to serve his sentence in the naval barracks. He was just nineteen years of age. He served his time with grace, dignity and impeccable behaviour and was to tell us many months later that the navy had taught him how to survive in the wild, and that shamefully he had had to steal food. He recalled that one horrendous night, a severe electrical storm, the worst he had ever known, nearly broke his nerve and somehow he managed to hitch-hike his way north and finally reach Tearo House.

Rob returned to his duties after serving his sentence, in the hope that the situation had been sorted out, but it seems his terrible ordeal had been in vain. He found that his career was blocked at every turn and his senior officer was intent on breaking his will. Rob was fighting a losing battle, and so, after another long year of setbacks and bullying behaviour, he fought his way to the top and demanded to be released from his six year contract.

Normally this cannot be done, but after a great deal of legal wrangling Rob was free. His commanding officer shook his hand and wished him well, then added confidentially that Rob had been 'set up' and that his hands had been tied This was some small consolation for Rob, I think. Within the year, at the age of twenty, he was on his way to a career of breathtaking danger, combined with technical skills and a mental strength that not many possess, as a diver in the oil fields of the Middle East. His naval experience had taught him to respect his fellow man, and as he rose to the top during his sixty years he has been well known for his overwhelming sense of fair play. He has dealt with a hugely diverse range of nationalities and saved many lives, both in and out of the water. He himself has had many brushes with death and his life reads like a James Bond novel. His dry sense of humour and self deprecating wit, combined with his great love of music and reading, make for an interesting man.

Meanwhile, although Sam did not say too much, I could see that things were not going that well between her and Bill. I, with my children, come from the generation of letter writers, and although Bill was still at sea, letters were flying fast and furious between him and Sam. As indeed, between myself and Father, but at a more gentle pace. Father's letters were always a joy to read, so descriptive and well put together.

Bill was struggling with the flooring business and the curse of floor laying men, damaged knee caps, seriously affected him.

Rob's dangerous life in the Middle East was a constant worry to me but Lucy's job at the pharmacy was becoming very interesting. Her times behind the counter provided many humorous anecdotes that caused great laughter at the dinner table. Pip, her constant companion, was also a close member of the family, along with all the other animals. Lucy would quite often ride Pip round to the back garden where we would all take our turn at petting this loveable animal.

But Sam was becoming bored, restless and unhappy. Bill was in constant pain and I was, as always, tired. So it was at this time of my life that I saw an apparition. It was early one autumnal morning, before I went to work. By now our sleeping arrangements had changed and we were in single beds. When I was working I was always the first to rise. I would leave my bed in the large room, then cross a small square landing, down a flight of stairs, across another large landing and into the bathroom. From there I would normally run quickly down the next flight of stairs to the hall, but for some strange reason that morning I glanced up to the landing above. The large window on my left produced enough light to see this floor quite clearly. And there he was! I froze with complete terror. He was a dwarf-like creature with a deformed right shoulder that was bent and twisted across his chest. He wore a pointed cap which fell over his right eye. His eyes were dark and burning with an evil and malicious intent, his bloodless lips were drawn back over yellowing teeth as he snarled and hissed pure venom at me. His dirty coat had tails rather like Grandpa's dress coat and his filthy claw-like hands were reaching out to me with cat like movements when playing with a mouse. As I stared, helplessly mesmerised by this creature, he began to move slowly toward me. He wanted to destroy me, of that I was certain, I had to escape! In my desperate haste to reach the kitchen I nearly fell down the next two flights of stairs. As I lit the gas fire and filled the kettle for a soothing cup of tea, my hands were shaking. What on earth had I seen? What on earth had just happened?

I was in no doubt that I had seen something, but what? This was not the usual idea of what constitutes a ghost-like figure. This was a manifestation of pure evil and it wanted to harm me. I thought long and hard for many months about what I had seen and felt that somewhere deep within the bowels of Tearo House there lay a force that was capable of destroying life.

Finally, Sam's marriage was over. Sadly divorce affects the rest of the family almost as much as the two people concerned, and so it was with my family. Lucy, in particular, was saddened by the break-up of her sister's marriage as she had become rather fond of Bill. There was no denying that Bill was an absolute charmer, with an engaging manner, and it was easy to see how he attracted the girls. My Bill was noncommittal about the whole affair, and all I wanted was for Sam to be happy. Bill and I had to attend a small court where we had to answer rather searching questions about the couple's relationship, and I found the part where I had 'to tell the whole truth' rather disconcerting. Bill and Sam were interviewed at length, there was much signing of official documents and very soon the whole affair was finalised.

Chapter Forty-one

When Rob came home on leave he would automatically return to his old room at Tearo House, but now he was out of the Royal Navy he had outgrown parental control and found a shabby flat in a very large old house nearby to Grange Road.

By this time the relationship between Bill and I was slowly and insidiously crumbling. We still kept up the pretence of a happy family but there were underlying tensions that could not be ignored. Sam and her baby were an extra expense on both Bill and myself and Bill was in constant pain with his troublesome kneecap. This meant that the business was dwindling and the outlook was bleak. Bill's bruised ego for letting yet another business slip though his fingers did not make for a happy man. And then Lucy had her accident.

It was a warm spring evening when we women were at home together. Sam was busy with her baby, I was in the kitchen feeding the animals and Lucy was rushing through the hair washing process. She knew she was in trouble, as she had come home later than the allotted time and I had made my displeasure quite plain in no uncertain words. With her long, thick hair wrapped in a towel, and barefoot, she rushed downstairs on her way to the kitchen. I heard her stumble on the last step and thought nothing of it until I saw on the tiled floor thick, black clots of glutinous blood. I called Sam, and on inspection we found Lucy's little toe was hanging loosely from her foot. When she slipped on the stairs the sharp edge of the solid oak spindle nearly sliced her little toe from her foot. We had to get her to hospital, but Bill had not yet returned and taxi fares were beyond my pocket. I was beginning to panic, as Lucy was in pain and losing blood. With the aid of yellow pages, Sam and I rang every public house in Stockdale, but Bill was nowhere to be found. Finally, in sheer desperation, Sam and I scraped together enough money for one journey, and with the help of the taxi driver we managed to lift Lucy into the car. I had to stay at home in case my six month old grandson should wake; and I needed to see Bill.

By the time Bill arrived I was burning with frustration, anger and almost hate. I had been pacing up and down in the garden while waiting for him, and when he finally arrived he was surprised to see me waiting outside. I hissed through gritted teeth, "Where the hell have you been, Bill? I have rung every pub in Stockdale and you weren't there. Where have you been?"

I watched the expression on his face slowly change from slight inebriation to incredulous guilt and I knew there and then that all I had been told about his infidelity was true. I brushed his pathetic explanation aside and explained what had happened. He seemed slightly dazed by the events and I had to make it clear that he had to go to the hospital to bring the girls home safely. After that shocking revelation my feelings for Bill changed. Until then, and in spite of the way he had controlled my life, I still loved him. But all that had changed.

By now it was obvious that Bill needed surgery on his knee, and on the day of the operation I found it difficult to concentrate on my work. To reach the hospital from my place of work meant a long and difficult journey. As it was nearing Christmas the bitter cold and dark nights made my journey home equally arduous, as a mile long walk was involved. However, I visited him every night for a week, even though the allotted hour was usually spent in an awkward silence. On the day of his release from the hospital he stumbled on the steps. I reached out instinctively to hold him, but he brushed me aside so roughly I nearly fell, and he said that he was not an invalid and to leave him alone. I felt quite tearful, but was also quite angry.

Bill's recovery was long and painful and made worse by his refusal to use either crutches or a stick. He began to complain to me about the extra cost incurred by Sam and her baby, and the atmosphere became so acrimonious that Sam and I were forced into finding her a job. Night work was all that was available under the circumstances, and so she became a barmaid at one of Stockdale's more genteel public houses. She very quickly became the star turn, with every drunk in town trying his luck with her. I took to sitting at one end of the bar with a gin and tonic, in order to keep an eye on any male that went too far, but I was becoming resentful at her having to do this kind of work and distinctly uneasy at the way men looked at her. After one particular incident, in which I had to forcibly intervene, I snapped and she handed in her notice. The manager was very sorry to see her go because takings had definitely improved while Sam worked there. However, Bill was not happy about losing the money she brought in, and another dreadful row ensued.

During this period Robbie's life had also taken a downward turn. While working in the Middle East for a large American oil company he had been ordered by the client to use some particular diving equipment and to perform certain procedures. Knowing that both the equipment and procedures would endanger life Robbie refused to complete the work. He went before the board and was interviewed at some length. This led to dismissal and blackballing. Not only this, but he was involved with various romantic entanglements. So, together with his father, he drowned his sorrows in the amber nectar.

After his operation, Bill still had one or two contracts to fulfil, so with Rob's help they completed the work together. It was not long before Rob was offered another position, as the word had gone round the diving fraternity and he was now respected for his integrity. So off he went to that world of unbearable heat, uneatable food and sandstorms. He faced danger at every turn, both on land and in the water, and ever so slowly he was becoming more and more of a stranger to me.

g

Chapter Forty-two

Sadly there was another problem I had to face. My eyesight had been causing me trouble for some time and, after numerous tests and weeks of treatment at the eye hospital, I was advised to change my work. This was a bitter blow. I was now in my forties and employment was difficult to find during the 1970s, particularly in the north east which had been hit badly with the closure of so many steelworks.

Miraculously Sam had found an excellent position in Stockdale's Council Housing Department which proved to be the luckiest break she ever had in her short life. The group of six women bonded together to such an extent that on one occasion I was almost envious of the affection they had for each other; but I never doubted Sam's love for me. We were close enough in age to be almost mistaken for sisters, and our relationship was deeper than that of mother and daughter. It should have been a happier time for us, but now that Robbie had returned to the Middle East Bill was moody and secretive, which in turn brought about in me a resentment and irritation at his irrational behaviour. Our marriage had never been one of shared activities and companionship, and I had never known of his daily movements but this was different. Nevertheless, I had my own bête noire to face and at the age of forty I had to find another job.

I was about to enter another world. It was that of a departmental store in the shape of our local Debenhams. I was to sell cameras, audio and hi-fi. All well and good, but I knew a little about cameras and absolutely nothing about hi-fi. My only 'system' was a battered old gramophone player that took vinyl which I had bought second hand some years previously. I was to work with two other employees. The manager, who knew everything about everything, or so it seemed, and a young trainee. My first week was absolute hell and I became exhausted and irritable, while trying to keep a peaceful atmosphere at home for my two girls. But Bill and I were rowing more than ever. There were at least two occasions when I had had to seek refuge in Sam's bed, hoping their presence would deter Bill from any physical violence. How I ever became an efficient, knowledgeable and persuasive sales person I will never know!

The atmosphere in a departmental store was very different to the slightly academic background I had known in my previous work. Here the talk in the tea room revolved round babies, husbands and boyfriends. I also learned about make-up, the latest fashion trend. To my surprise I discovered I was attractive to other men. I had never thought of myself as beautiful, as Bill had never passed comment one way or the other, so I began to enjoy the attention, flattery and innocent flirtations.

While I was trying to adapt to life in a shop, Sam had befriended a local boy and he became a regular visitor to Tearo House. Bill seemed to accept him and Sam was cautiously happy about the relationship. She told me she would only marry again if I approved of her choice. This was a heavy responsibility, but when I looked into her eyes shining with love how could I not agree. Marriage was discussed and we were to meet Jack's parents. I even bought a new tea tray with which to carry my assortment of cups and saucers to the sitting room. The six of us perched uneasily on the edge of my shabby furniture, with 'pinkies' to the ready. Our lips stretched into frozen smiles; we were ready for battle! It was obviously a case of whether or not this girl, with a child, was good enough for their young and adored son.

I bristled! Outraged by the slightest suggestion of a slur on my daughter's character, I very quickly put them straight on that point. Jack's mother was an Irish matriarch and reigned supreme over her brood of six children, but I made it clear that, in me, she had met her match. In spite of disliking the woman, I had to admit they were a very close and loving family and had a solid outlook on life. Jack was an ambitious British Telecom Engineer and I felt Sam's future would be safe in his hands.

The courtship continued until they found that within the next few months their combined salaries would be enough to put down a deposit on a mortgage. Lucy and I were thrilled, and even Bill muted some congratulatory grunts about their future.When the most perfect house was up for sale they jumped at the chance. A nerve-racking few weeks passed and then they were the proud owners of their own home The solid three bedroomed semi was in a small cul-de-sac only twenty minutes walk from Grange Road. It really was perfect.

At last life was improving for my child. Sadly it was not the case for Bill and myself. Our rows were becoming deeply emotional and even physical. A great deal of ornaments and crockery were smashed, which I could ill afford!

On one occasion Robbie was home on leave, and as he was between flats was sleeping in his old room. A row broke out between us and Bill was so enraged he threw his bed at me as I lay in mine. My screams of anger were so distressing that Robbie had to intervene. He took his father down to the kitchen and did his best to calm him down, while I sought refuge in the girl's bedroom.

Robbie found his new flat, a little closer to Grange Road this time, then returned to the Middle East for yet another long spell.

My uneasy marriage continued much as usual, I went my way and Bill went his. I became used to having Jack around the house, as they were redecorating their new home. Arrangements for their marriage were delayed until furnishing and decor were completed to their satisfaction.

Christmas was approaching and I was rather disgruntled to find I was to work late on Christmas Eve to prepare for the Boxing Day sale, on which day I also had to work.

Christmas Day arrived, Jack was with us, and Lucy's boyfriend was to come for the afternoon. I thought everything was fairly normal until, after the meal, I saw Bill's car leaving the drive. He did not return that evening and the young ones were perplexed and uncertain as to how to approach me. But by then I simply did not care.

Boxing Day found me at nine o'clock with my colleagues ready for the action in Debenhams' store, but I was completely unprepared for what was to follow. The big double doors opened on the stroke of nine, and within seconds the ground floor was a

148

seething mass of excited, grabbing, thrusting, and demanding people intent on securing their prize. They swirled shoulder to shoulder, jammed together, pushing and shoving, and demanding immediate service from me and my colleagues as we sheltered behind a small counter. I swung into professional mode and coped with customer after customer, demonstrating, selling and wrapping up. The pressure was relentless as hour after hour went on and on.

All was done with a happy smile and a merry quip, but the nagging thought at the back of my mind was, had Bill done something really stupid and how would I stand with the law if he had? I began to tire and the building was overheating. I became hotter and hotter, until things began to fade and I heard a commanding voice in the distance clearing people aside and calling for a chair.

As luck would have it the customer I was serving was a doctor. I tried to apologise for making a fuss by explaining I was worried about my husband who had walked out on Christmas Day and not returned. Then things became really complicated as the police were called in. I was taken into a small room, questioned at great length, and was told they had contacted Sam and she had a number to ring when her father returned. I thanked them for their understanding and returned to the shop floor.

The next day I found I was the subject of highly colourful gossip, and the security man, a retired policeman of some note, greeted me with a smile and an offer 'to go and fill Bill in'. Apparently the police considered this deed to be the most despicable crime a man could commit without good reason.

Bill turned up two days later and just before the time I was given to report him as a missing person. There was no apology, no explanation, and yet he still had the power to make me feel responsible in some way.

I continued with my work at the store, and although there was a great deal of comradeship, laughter and fascinating gossip to be enjoyed, I did not feel altogether comfortable with the work. Another drawback was the restricting shop hours. As previously mentioned, when I was employed by British Steel Research and Brackenborough Borough Council I would leave the girls with Bill and after finishing work on Friday, take the midnight coach from Stockdale High Street to London, then the train to Brighton, the bus to Telscombe Cliffs, and then walk up the hill to my parent's bungalow. I would spend Saturday evening and most of Sunday with my parents. I would then repeat the return night journey, arriving in Stockdale in the early hours of Monday morning in order to be at my work on time. I took this exhausting journey many, many times, as the bond between my parents and myself was so binding I did it all willingly. I continued with the journey after Mother died, for the sake of my father, but when I was employed by the store the journey was no longer possible.

Life continued at Tearo House but the tension between Bill and myself was growing stronger. It was only the girls' cheerful banter and positive outlook that kept the family group together.

However, when Robbie was home on leave the two men would drink together. Bill had done his disappearing act again and had been moody and secretive ever since, but one evening he went too far. The girls and I were all in the bathroom preparing for bed. As I have explained, the bathroom was a place in which to chat, and I was having my bath when the door burst open and Bill staggered in. He muttered some unintelligible obscenities at us and then suddenly and shockingly spat on my naked back as I cowered in the bath. He then laughingly used the lavatory and staggered out to join Robbie in the kitchen.

Lucy fled from the bathroom, and as Sam tenderly washed his spittle from me we could still hear their drunken voices from below. I tried to laugh it off for Sam's sake, but she was a woman now and understood only too well.

Chapter Forty-three

Sam would be leaving soon, as her wedding was finally arranged. This was not to be the lavish affair of her first wedding, but instead a simple ceremony at the registry office followed by a small buffet at Tearo House. One of Jack's sisters very kindly made and exquisitely iced a magnificent wedding cake in Wedgewood Blue, and another sister provided a mixed selection of sandwiches, while I provided the finishing touches. I had also been busy at the sewing machine and made a discreet bridal dress for Sam. With a matching brimmed hat over her heavy blonde bob she looked truly beautiful.

Bill played a very subdued part all through the procedure, drinking the champagne only on sufferance as beer was his preferred drink. I had to admit the Balfour clan were a force to be reckoned with. As they swarmed into Tearo House like inquisitive bees looking for their queen, all the while exclaiming about the size of my home, the stairs and the quirky kitchen, I too found myself drifting into the shadows away from their constant chatter. I was also a bit miffed about the way Jack's mother insisted on keeping my three-year-old grandson firmly by her side during the ceremony. Suffice to say he broke away from her as soon as we entered Tearo House and quickly mingled with his family. But this was Sam's day, and as I watched her glowing with happiness I could only pray that this marriage would work.

As Sam and Jack settled into their new home we found it quite exciting to have another house to visit. They were only twenty minutes walk away and in spite of our busy lives we managed to see each other quite often.

Inevitably, Lucy was becoming streetwise and bringing home, shall we say, some interesting boyfriends. Sam and I kept a close eye on my little imp and the antics in which she was becoming involved as she was a complete innocent in the world of boys. She was more interested in animals of any description, and her beloved Pip took up a great deal of her time. Then a certain young man was appearing more frequently and I began to suspect he could be 'the one'! When she told me extremely casually that he had been allowed to tread the hallowed ground of the field and actually entered the 'inner sanctum' of Pip's stable, I knew it was tantamount to telling me that she had chosen her man. She was also to tell me, some weeks later, that on one occasion she and Tom had been riding bareback in the field. Knowing he was terrified of the animal, she spurred Pip on to an even greater speed. After a while the animal began to tire, so laughing and giggling she headed him for the stable. With one exhilarating burst of energy they hurled toward the stable door. Leaving only a second to spare, my incorrigible daughter screamed 'DUCK'. Too late, as Tom's shoulder crunched against the wooden post of the door and down he went. The memory of that moment still provokes her giggling even though I expressed shock at what could have been a serious accident.

Of course, the inevitable happened and Lucy became pregnant. Oh, my poor Lucy, it was all so different to her sister's pregnancy and I felt quite helpless. Happily Sam's pregnancy had been relatively trouble free and there were days when she had positively glowed. Because she had worked for her uncle, Bill's brother, the architect, he and his partners spoiled her as if she were their own daughter.

Sadly Lucy became withdrawn, pale and strained with her pregnancy, and when she finally told me, four months later, I could hear in her voice guilt, shame and defiance. One must remember this was still the 1970s and society was not yet as accepting of the single mother as today.

For reasons known only to herself, Lucy was adamant she was not going to marry Tom, and indeed did not until four years later. She defiantly declared she would manage somehow. There was a strong independent streak in Lucy, born from an insecure childhood, but hidden deep within was a heartbreaking vulnerability.

Sam and I cared and supported her, and did our best to keep her positive, but she had to sell Pip. She knew she could not afford to keep him and bring up a child as well, so her beloved animal had to go. It simply broke her heart.

However, as her time grew closer, Tom became very supportive of her. And so I was to spend one bitterly cold March night with Tom at the hospital when Lucy's labour began. It was long and hard and she haemorrhaged badly, but finally my second grandchild was born. True to my premonition with Sam, there she was, my little baby girl with a shock of black hair. Tom and I were jubilant at the news, and after a short time with her we said good bye to my exhausted daughter, never suspecting the horror that was to follow.

South Moor Hospital was a relatively new building; extra units and improvements were constantly ongoing. There had been trouble with an intricate wiring system to one particular unit and rumours of inefficient workmanship were spreading. The night my granddaughter was born a blizzard of such ferocity, the like of which surprised even the locals, hit that corner of the north east. The strength of the wind, the heavy snowfall and the plummeting temperatures were not usually known at this time of year. In the second floor ward of new mothers, Lucy was at last sleeping deeply after giving birth, when she was suddenly woken by a terrified nurse screaming, "Fire! There is a fire. You all have to get out. Just pick up your babies and run. Just get out!"

There was no time for dressing gowns or slippers. So Lucy, with the other shocked mothers, ran. Clutching her baby in one arm, blinded by driving snow, she made her way precariously down an icy metal fire escape. On reaching the ground they then, still barefoot, had to cross a snow-covered forecourt before finally reaching a reception area. Then they waited, shivering with shock and freezing temperatures, until beds were hastily made up for the poor girls.

It was a terrifying ordeal and Lucy was unable to find out quite what had happened. There were rumours that trouble in the laundry, beneath the baby ward, had caused the fire to spread rapidly before help arrived. Lucy took quite some time to recover from her experience, as her feet were badly cut and bruised. She also contracted a very heavy cold.

With any emotional upheaval Lucy would either laugh it off or else would not speak of any trouble until much later. Consequently she has only recently told me just how horrifying it had been.

So there I was again! At home with another dependant daughter and child. I was perfectly happy to have my child and her baby to look after, but Bill was growing older. The thought of yet another baby and all the disruption they cause was beginning to irritate him. Samantha was thrilled with her baby niece and helped in any little way that she could, but like most people there was not a great deal to spare from the family budget. I continued to work the long hours at Debenhams and naturally helped as much as I could with the extra cost to Bill. Tom also did his best to support Lucy and his baby daughter, as he was thrilled with his little girl. The terrible arguments between Bill and myself continued and as always I did my best to protect Lucy and her baby from the worst of the outbursts.

The constant accusations of my imagined infidelity began when living in the cottage. At first his jealousy made me feel rather special and loved, but as he began to include the milkman and any other male with which I came into contact in the long list of my lovers, I became unsure of how to handle him. My so obviously innocent and tearful protestations seemed to provoke his overwhelming sense of self-pity into yet more hurtful accusations. I also lived in constant fear, when the children were small, that he would cease to provide a home for us if I did not comply with his wishes. But when the children had grown to adulthood, a couple of incidents occurred that made me realise how far Bill would go to come between me and them. One involved Robbie when he was on leave from the Navy and he and his father would drink together. Samantha was still at home, as she was yet to marry, and as usual we were in the bathroom happily chatting prior to going to bed. Suddenly a drunken and outraged Robbie burst into the room shouting and screaming that as I was earning such a vast amount of money it was my duty to give more to his poor father who was doing his best to keep a roof over my head. My instant and instinctive reaction was to hit him hard across his cheek. Such an unlikely action of mine shocked us both. And after muttering at me incoherently for some time, he finally left the room.

Chapter Forty-four

Many months later, after Sam and Jack were married and living in their own home, another more worrying incident happened. I was alone in the bathroom, as Lucy was spending the evening with Sam, when Robbie burst through the door. But this time was different. This time he was holding a vicious looking knife in his hand! His drunken ramblings were of my infidelity to his loving and faithful father and that he would kill me and any man he saw me with.

However, I was not going to argue with a drunken man holding a knife, so managed to dodge under his arms, which were thrashing about in uncontrollable anger, run down the stairs and out of the open front door. I practically ran all the way to the safety of Sam's home where I collapsed with shock from the trauma I had just experienced. Lucy returned to her father later that evening, but I stayed on for a few days. I had a great deal of thinking to do.

I was beginning to feel pure hate for this man I had trusted and loved for so many years. I felt utter contempt toward him for drip feeding such poison about me to my young son. Conversely I was not going to justify my marriage to Robbie. If he wished to believe his father then so be it! But I could not deny the pain I felt from the strained relationship between myself and Robbie.

On returning to Tearo House I found it almost impossible to control my anger with Bill. In a voice shaking with emotion I told him of my fury at his actions. I also said that although I wished to leave him I new legally I would lose everything. As I was forced to stay I was withdrawing from all marital duties and would live my life my own way. Overcome with emotion, I added tearfully that I would never speak to him again. He listened with sardonic contempt and had little to say in reply.

As time went by, I realised to my horror that Lucy was taking over the household duties. That I had put her in such a position nearly destroyed me. So it was no great surprise when three months later, on coming home from work, she told me the district nurse had called to see her. It transpired that Lucy might be eligible for a home of her own. I suspect that Lucy, understandably, had told the nurse of the acrimonious atmosphere between her parents.

By now Samantha held an important position in the local council housing department and was able to secure the key to a delightful council house for Lucy. So the next evening the three of us went to view the property and found it to be absolutely perfect. It had been built on the estate behind the church at the top of Grange Road and was only twenty minutes walk from Tearo House. This estate was built on farmland where I had played as a small child and was attractively landscaped. Lucy's house had an unusually large garden, both back and front, and looked onto a large open play area. My relief and joy at having both my beloved daughters housed so close to Grange Road was overwhelming. My life might have been in chaos but I had my girls around me and could wish for nothing more.

Somehow, together, Samantha, myself and even Bill managed to furnish Lucy's new home. As soon as Tom moved in Lucy's single mother's benefit stopped and they were reliant on the family allowance and Tom's humble wage as a lorry driver to pay the rent. In order to support her sister, Sam paid the going rate of a nursery to Lucy on the proviso that she looked after Sam's young son Andy. This arrangement worked very well and the two young couples grew close to each other. Even though Lucy was happily settled she seemed reluctant to marry. I did not pursue the matter, knowing she would come to a decision in her own good time.

My life with Bill took on a new routine, it became an upstairs, downstairs arrangement, Bill living predominately in the kitchen while I made the playroom my sanctuary. Bill bought himself a small television set for the kitchen, where he was warm and comfortable. I rented a small portable set for the playroom, where it was cold and draughty. By this time I had left the marital bed and Bill did not bother me ever again. I would rise early in the morning, breakfast, quickly tidy round the house then leave for the long journey to work. On my return, Bill would have a small evening meal ready for me which I would eat from a tray. Each evening I would take a very large gin and tonic to the bathroom. While running a hot bath I would listen to my radio and write my diary. Bill would surface after I had left for work in the morning, but as his life seemed to have drifted into semi-retirement I neither knew nor cared where he went or what he did. From where the money came had been a mystery all my life, but he always seemed to pay his way. I paid a small weekly rent, which was a drop in the ocean as to the running costs of Tearo House. Any communication that was necessary was done through the girls. Fortunately they had accepted the situation, although they wished it was not so. Lucy continued to cope with Bill's laundry, and from what I could gather Bill spent quite some time at her home. With the girls co-operation this arrangement seemed to work reasonably well, until it came to Christmas.

Bill's controlling nature affected not only myself but also his daughters. Christmas was always to be spent at home, as he enjoyed preparing the turkey the night before. While the foul was cooking he would visit the pub then arrive home full of Christmas spirit. Even when the girls had their own homes he insisted that the two families spent Christmas at Tearo House. It was when we were finally seated at the kitchen table the situation became almost farcical.

"Ask your mother if she wants turkey," Bill would ask the girls. My frosty reply was returned in the same childish manner.

But worst of all was Mark's Christmas visit. Each year Mark and his family would travel up from Leeds, where they had spent Christmas with Prue's parents, to spend a whole day at Tearo House. Bill had always resented my close relationship with Mark. When Mark married Prue, Bill found it difficult to disguise his dislike of the girl. Oh, how I dreaded these days! Even when the children were small and I was relatively happy, Bill's welcome was distinctly cool. But when my marriage changed, and after one terribly strained visit, Mark discreetly excused himself and Prue from continuing the little tradition. To everybody's great relief, I might add! In order to spend time with my brother I began to visit him in his own home.

In fact, I began to spread my wings and spend time with my southern relatives. As already mentioned, by now Father was settled in an old people's home in Seaford. Luckily the bungalow had not yet been sold, thereby enabling me to stay in it. I would make the long overnight journey to Brighton. I collected the bungalow key from a neighbour, turned on the water, lit a coal fire, then made another bus journey to Seaford. The old people's home, although adequate, was a gloomy old place, but Father was well looked after. It had originally been a convent, and my poor father was like a fish out of water. It broke my heart to see him there, but my sisters-in-law had both flatly refused to have him stay with them.

I had offered Father a home at Grange Road but his hatred of Stockdale prevented him from accepting. He was rather a stubborn old man, I suppose. One lovely afternoon at Seaford I booked a taxi to take us to the seafront and then collect us later on. We had a large ice cream cornet then sat in a shelter on the front. We sat quietly together, watching and listening to the rhythmical gentle whoosh and soft hiss of frothy white waves breaking on a shingled shore. We were both lost in our own thoughts, unable to communicate verbally with each other, but strangely I felt closer to him than I had done for quite some time.

Later I was thankful for that afternoon in the sun at Seaford, for I was to see him only twice more in less happier circumstances. He had a heart attack and was in hospital for quite some time before he finally died from cancer.

Chapter Forty-five

Still working at Debenhams, I began to join in the social activities arranged for the staff. Christmas parties were the highlight of the year. My previous employers had them, although on a much smaller scale. One year I attended a Medieval Banquet at a baronial hall in Northumberland. It was all very authentic and highly exciting. I certainly enjoyed myself that night.

But my happiest time with the store was The Fashion Show. The show was organised, produced and directed by the store's window dresser Nigel. I was asked to participate as the 'older woman'. Not very flattering, I fear, as I was only forty-two, but I was ready to party!

And what enormous fun I had! Nigel excelled at his work, for I would watch him while he created the most amazing montages, and his waspish sense of humour and untiring energy brought out the best in our little team. There were eight of us and we met only twice. Once to meet each other and the second time to walk through our positions. The event was to be held in a large storeroom at the back of the building and was to advertise the latest designs in Ladies Wear.

The evening arrived, every seat was taken and the cat walk looked very professional, all due to Nigel's organisational skills. The store's make-up girl was there to make us up while we models had a dresser to help with the changes. The young girls had volunteered happily to take part, believing their prowess on the dance floor to be more than adequate for the show. Whereas I could not put one foot in front of the other, but still felt I could walk well.

The show opened with Day Wear. My dress was rather plain, with short sleeves and a full skirt. I did not much care for it but nothing would deter me from enjoying every moment. Unfortunately, the younger girls lost their nerve and began to stumble awkwardly.

For the Short Evening Wear I was paired with another girl, Paula. We both wore short, full-skirted black silk dresses. Paula's was sleeveless with a modest neckline and a small waist. Mine had long sleeves with a high neckline that fell from my shoulders to my bikini line, leaving my back completely exposed. We wore red high heeled shoes, black stockings and carried red and gold handbags. A cheeky little red beret perched on top of our thick hair and ropes of pearls hung round our necks. "Think French Tarts," Nigel laughingly told us! Now bear in mind I had given birth to three children and breastfed them all, and I last wore a bathing costume on Brighton beach, so this display of near nudity was a little daunting.

The music began, and taking a deep breath we were off. We sashayed seductively down to centre front, twirling our pearls and swinging our handbags. There we posed gracefully with dazzling smiles to the audience, and then my moment came as, with a very naughty little smile, I slowly turned to reveal my naked back. There was a slight gasp, then laughter, then wild applause as I gave it my all. Then laughing, giggling, and wriggling everything I had, we danced gaily together off the stage.

I was to close the show displaying the older woman's Bridal Gown, and I will never forget those precious twelve minutes on the cat walk. This time my gown was long sleeved, with a modest neckline and full skirt. A wide-brimmed hat matched the lacework on the dress and white satin shoes completed the outfit. The music was slow and melodic; a piece by Elton John. I was completely lost in the lilting tones, and found myself swaying dreamily from side to side, lightly holding the heavy skirts to reveal my beautiful shoes, before poising almost reverently centre stage.

Then, with a naughty smile from beneath the brim of my hat, I sashayed seductively down the aisle to more applause and the anonymity of the backstage.

The show was a great success, all due to Nigel's artistic skills, and when the store's magazine was published most of the photographs were, embarrassingly, of myself!

During the years working for Debenhams, my relationship with Robbie was distant at the best of times. Various young girlfriends were brought to Grange Road to meet his father. One or two he would introduce to me rather icily when I was home during the evenings. Most of them were the kind of girl I would not wish to introduce to my family. On one occasion a rather over confident bright young thing gurgled politely, "Oh, you are not nearly as bad as they said you were!" I find it difficult to express my feelings after that little '*bon mot*'! However, one particularly brittle girl seemed to be around more than most. One day I was confronted by Bill to tell me he was going to file for divorce. Apparently he, Robbie and the said girl had been plotting to build a granny flat for Bill on the back of the house where the scullery had been. Robbie and the girl were to live in the house, and together they would share the upkeep of the old place.

To say I was astounded would be an understatement! At first I was not sure how to react! Was I relieved or was I angry? I really was not sure. I said nothing to the girls, knowing how Bill's plans always crumbled at the last minute. But, true to his word, some weeks later my divorce papers came through. I must admit I felt a little strange: relieved, but rather frightened as to what the future may hold.

However, that morning Lucy called at Grange Road and I told her that we were going to divorce, and that the papers had just arrived. Her immediate reaction was so violent, such a terrible cry for help, such heartbreaking pain. I was completely shocked and stunned into silence by the agony in her voice as she ran out of the house crying, "I hate you. I hate you. I will never come to this house again."

I left her alone for a couple of days, knowing that Sam was with her. When I next saw her in her own home she was calmer and more understanding of the situation; to my great relief, I might add.

Within the next week Bill told me the divorce was cancelled and their plans for a granny flat had fallen through. Robbie's relationship with the girl was on the rocks also. I should have realised, knowing Bill, that he would back out of any situation whereby he would be perceived as the 'bad guy'. That would never do!

I was greatly saddened by the entire episode, as I had tasted freedom and now my chance had gone. Nevertheless, losing my freedom had conversely given Lucy greater piece of mind and that was all that really mattered.

Chapter Forty-six

Although I had quite enjoyed working at Debenhams I was restless and needed a change. I had made new friends, experienced greater challenges and worked within a very different background, but I was desperate for change in my life. So when I saw a position for supervisor and buyer advertised in the local arts and crafts shop I jumped at the chance. In spite of a complete lack of experience in the skills of stock control and buying, when interviewed by the boss himself, I was offered the job. This must have been the only rash decision this affable hard-headed businessman of Jewish origins had ever made in his life.

In a whirl of balance sheets, acquainting myself with an enormous range of stock, and meeting new people, I joined yet another world. I was to work there for nearly seven years and enjoyed every moment. There was bickering and tittle-tattle between a staff of eight women, of course, but overall we worked well together. Mr Jacobs came in every day to the office where he was aided by two other women to help with the mountainous paperwork. This was still the 1970s we must remember.

The shop was in the same town as Debenhams, just one block away, so my travelling routine was the same as before. It was also just across the road from the art college that I had longed to attend all those years ago. There were two departments; upstairs sold stationery and was run by Mrs Mac, while my ground floor department sold art materials and crafts.

I became completely immersed in this challenging and interesting work and would arrive home drained of all energy;

sometimes with sheer frustration or, alternatively, satisfaction at a job well done.

My life at home moved slowly into a calmer routine. I finally relinquished my life-long yearning for a home filled with pretty things of my own choosing and contented myself by moving furniture around and adding my own small touches. Happily the drudgery of cleaning and lighting coal fires had long gone and the sitting room now sported a large electric fire with log burning effects. I bought from a neighbour a coffee table she no longer wanted and I felt it helped to improve the room. Bill continued with his life in the kitchen and still provided my evening meals, for which I was particularly grateful. He was drifting into old age long before his time and began to take an interest in cooking. Sam would happily discuss various recipes with him as she was turning into a 'foodie' herself. With her help Bill began to extend his menus. He also took on other hobbies, marquetry being a strong favourite. I continued to clean the old house and tend the garden. I could not ignore the mess that came from wet cats and dogs.

My one great joy was when my darling girls, with the children, came to Tearo House at the weekends in order to spend time together. Sam and the children would sit in the kitchen with Bill for a while, leaving Lucy with me. I gather she saw enough of her father during the week. Looking back on my life with Bill, this had to be the most precious time of all. I never ceased to be thankful to have my daughters living in such close proximity to Grange Road. Life could so easily have taken them far away. We would celebrate all the usual family anniversaries; birthdays Halloween and Christmas, but it was just the normal get together for girlie chats that meant so very much. I just adored listening to my two girls teasing each other in the only way that loving sisters can. The love between Mother and Beth had had such a powerful influence on my childhood. I had always longed for a sister, but watching my two girls together helped to satisfy that youthful yearning.

In some strange way, because Bill and I had spoken openly about divorce it seemed to 'clear the air' as it were. I think he understood the marriage was over. All that overpowering love and trust I had felt for him had gone completely. All we had between us were the children, but the fear remained. That cold numbing fear would never leave as long as he was under the same roof.

How he felt toward me I was never to know. Bill was always too mindful of public disapproval to allow his real feelings to show. Somehow he seemed content to lead a separate life simply because the very structure of the house enabled two people to live together without the close contact that could lead to angry confrontation.

I have now lived long enough to observe the influence this old house had on three generations of women. There is something in the very bones of the building that inspires an almost love/hate relationship with him. His magic is still influencing the forth and fifth generation. He surely is a force with which to be reckoned. But I digress!

Robbie's affairs of the heart continued to cause concern. When on leave he was still very much under his father's influence, so our relationship remained distant. He was now in his third decade and suffering yet again from a badly bruised heart. His exploits overseas gave me sleepless nights and to a certain extent still do. However, one evening, when I was at home and busy with my sewing machine, a new girl was tentatively introduced to me by Robbie. Sam and Lucy told me later that she was five years older than him, married and with two children, and how, in spite of Robbie's ability to inspire great loyalty and respect from the men with whom he worked in his civilian life, he was distressingly naive towards his fellow man. I kept my thoughts to myself!

While Robbie was away and his flat was empty, Bill would disappear for a night quite unexpectedly. No reason was offered and I did not enquire. After all, that was the arrangement.

Meanwhile I was acquainting myself with my new working life. After a very shaky start I became familiar with a bewildering range of crafts and fancy goods, most of which were new to me, apart from the art materials, of course. As I became comfortable in my new skin, I found I thoroughly enjoyed the work and the people with whom I was working.

I enjoyed meeting a widely diverse range of customers and was soon to discover that when the employment figures dropped, which they did on a regular basis, the sales of frame making materials, in particular, rose. This hobby was seen to be better suited to burly steelworkers than macramé work and rug making. The highlight of the year was when Mr Jacobs entrusted me with an almost open cheque book at the large Art and Craft exhibition that was held in London every year. My travel and board were paid for two nights and it was then I learnt how to party!

The years were slipping by with absorbing and exhausting days at work. I was deeply involved in the daily lives of my two girls and my grandchildren, and Robbie's new girlfriend was becoming a regular visitor to Tearo House. During Robbie's leave I would be regaled by raucous laughter coming from the kitchen, when, with Bill, they were all drinking together. I had hoped nothing would come of this relationship, but eventually I was proved to be wrong.

Samantha and Jack were both busy with their careers. Jack was taking a great number of exams, while Sam was steadily climbing to the top in the local Housing Department. Lucy and Tom, in spite of not owning all the expected luxuries of today, were a contented little family.

Sadly Lucy was still pining for Pip, the great love of her life, and took a long time to recover. Strangely she was not yet ready to marry Tom who was still without his own door key. Lucy was having serious gynaecological problems, and after she lost the baby, Sam and I were very worried about her health. With time, and great support from myself and Sam, she slowly recovered and became pregnant again. It was during this pregnancy she finally decided to marry Torn. The wedding was a very simple affair in the registry office, with only Lucy's best friend and Tom's brother as witnesses. She did not want us there, but I looked after Sarah during the ceremony and Sam put out a little spread at her home.

So Lucy and Tom were married on a Tuesday, and after all the drinks and delicious food had been consumed, Tom went back to work. I felt rather sad about the whole arrangement, although I also understood my deeply thinking daughter.

Lucy's baby was due in December, so, one bitterly cold night two weeks before Christmas, I found myself watching the dawn break over frost covered cars in the parking space at South Moor Hospital. It was another bad birth, but Tom and I were kept well away from the delivery room. When a baby boy was born, Tom was overjoyed, understandably, but I was exhausted with tears of joy and relief.

Chapter Forty-seven

I had kept in touch with Holly and her husband, and her little girl was just a few months older than my grandson. It was an honour to be asked to be Jayne's godmother and I found the Catholic christening service to be an interesting ceremony. Sadly, I had missed Andy's christening as he had been christened on the *Ark Royal* in Portsmouth. It had been arranged rather quickly, when a gap in the ship's itinerary became available, and Bill, Lucy and myself were not able to be there in time.

On the subject of churches, ever since being excommunicated from my church I found myself visiting any other church rather than St. Andrews, even though it had played such an important part in my childhood.

Holly had passed her driving test while we had worked together and by now was a very competent driver. I used to stay overnight at her home and the next day we would find a country pub in which to have a snack. Holly and Harvey understood my marital situation and very innocently introduced me to one or two single men friends of theirs. However, it was not to be, with not even a spark of attraction. I felt uncomfortable with the arrangement because, after all, I was still married.

I was forty-seven years old when the call came from my sister-in-law, James's wife, to say that Father was seriously ill and asking for me.

By now the bungalow had been sold, so it was arranged that I would travel to Mark's home and then both of us would drive to Seaford. Prue ran a tight ship domestically, and the imminen demise of Father, which necessitated my presence, proved to be rather inconvenient. Consequently the atmosphere was rather frosty, which in turn did not improve my mood. On top of which I had a terrible head cold and did not feel too well. Fortunately I was only there one night. It was a long drive from the village where Mark lived just outside Northampton to Seaford, where Father was in hospital.

It was a relief to be with Mark, and as we understood each other's minds speech was not really necessary. When we arrived at the hospital it was obvious Father was dying, and I was overwhelmed by a gut-wrenching sadness. Although frail, he was quite a big man and he was lying on a bed with side rails. When I enquired as to their use, he almost managed a chuckle as he told me, "They are to stop me falling out, lassie." Mark found it all too distressing and kept disappearing. I stayed by the bedside holding Father's hand all afternoon until, with a breaking heart, I had to say good bye.

It was a sad and thoughtful journey back to the village, and I was heartily thankful to be with Mark at that particular time. It was the beginning of October, and when, ten days later, I had to ask Mr Jacobs for time off for the funeral he was not too pleased.

By now my grief had settled down on me like a dark cloud and, having to also cope with Mr Jacobs's displeasure, I found it difficult to keep my emotions under control. It was to be my last journey to Brighton, and the whole affair was becoming a nightmare. The London coach left from the next town, seven miles away at 8.00 a.m., so the day before the funeral I either had to take a taxi or ask Bill for a lift.

My budget for the whole trip was so tight I had to ask Bill for the favour. When he told me he would be out that night and could not make it in the morning I was near to tears. Arriving home from work that evening the house was cold and dark and it was raining heavily. After I made sandwiches for the journey and packed my overnight bag I poured myself a stiff gin and tonic. As I listened to the wind howling round the old house it was as if he mirrored my pain and grief, and fury with Bill. How could he put this other woman before me under such sad circumstances? Surely, after forty years of marriage, he could have shown a little compassion.

The wind grew stronger and the old sash windows began to

rattle in their wooden frames. Huge gusts of wind were thrown against the brick walls and I began to feel nervous in that large empty house. Sitting by the fireside, listening to the soft hiss of the gas fire with the whole world crashing around me, I had never felt so alone as I did that night.

When I finally arrived in Brighton I had to find somewhere to stay. The cold was so intense it sapped my energy and all I could think of was to find a warm room. I knocked on the door of the first guest house from the station and it proved to be a lucky choice.

On hearing of my plight the proprietors did their best to make me feel comfortable. They even provided a hot-water bottle which was a godsend for my frozen feet. Father was to be buried with Mother in Telscombe Village, some fifteen miles from Brighton. This ancient village with its Saxon church was one of our special places to visit when staying at the bungalow. The next morning I had time to kill before the funeral and, as the temperature was dropping alarmingly for the south coast, I bought myself a stylish woollen hat to keep out the awful cold. Finally it was time to find a taxi to take me to the village, hoping I had enough money for the fare.

The driver dropped me at the top of the deserted village street from where I could see my large family group chatting quietly together. As I walked down the small slope they all turned and watched as I approached. I was closely related to every one of these people. My brothers, aunts, uncles and cousins. But once again I was overcome by that frightening sense of loneliness. James and his wife had organised the funeral, and before I knew it, it was time for me to travel back to Victoria and then on to Stockdale. Records were to show it had been the coldest November night for many years, and not long after the coach had begun our five hour journey north the heating system broke down.

My grief and despair was complete. Inwardly I cried and cursed and shivered and huddled into my big winter coat, which provided little or no protection against the merciless cold, until we finally reached Stockdale.

A few weeks later, on my day off, I was shopping in town when I bumped into Sam who was taking her lunch hour. I had of course, seen both the girls since the funeral, but this day Sam' arms were full of huge bunches of beautiful flowers. She explained that the girls at work had clubbed together as one of their colleagues had recently lost her father. She began to hesitate as she realised what she had said. There was a moment's silence and then she burst out, "Oh Mum, I know I should have gone with you. I am so very sorry. Will you ever forgive me? Come round tonight and we will have a chat," and with that she had gone.

I suppose I should have told her how unhappy I had been, but the moment passed and it was too late.

h

Chapter Forty-eight

My fiftieth birthday was approaching and luckily I was not to force what was to come before that memorable day.

Robbie's new girl, Rosie, had become part of the family and they were now living together. Because of her influence my relationship with my son was slowly improving and the powerful hold Bill had over Robbie was having to give way to Rosie's demands.

Lucy and Tom, with their children, seemed to be relatively happy, and I enjoyed babysitting for them whenever they could afford a night out. Tom was working for a small one-man business and in his spare time had helped his boss with a very heavy job in the garden. As a reward for his help, Tom had been given his first car; a worn out Volkswagen Beetle. This vehicle was dropping to pieces, but with Tom's loving care it was to give them at least another year's service, so they were able to make good use of this odd little car.

One fine weekend they invited me to join them in their trip to a local beauty spot in the country. Overnight rain had left large puddles, and as we rode through the narrow country lanes, gales of laughter would be heard from Lucy and myself. I was sitting with the children in the back, and to avoid a drenching from the puddles beneath we had to lift up our legs. Poor Tom simply had to be wet. Lucy and I still reminisce happily about the little trips we had in the old boneshaker.

However, things were not running quite as smoothly for Samantha and Jack. They were both deeply involved in their respective careers. Jack was taking many exams in order to further his position in the company and Sam was steadily working her way to the top of the Housing Department. They led busy lives, and luckily Lucy was always there for Andy when his parents were so busy. But I could sense a little tension between them. Sam earned a great deal more than Jack and she also loved pretty clothes, and I felt it odd that she would come to me for money with which to buy another little top she desired.

In the meantime Bill had been concerned about the wiring in the old house. As usual he employed men who supposedly were electricians and who charged accordingly. To say it had been disruptive did not exactly describe the nightmare of grit, dust, plaster and general mayhem that followed. Eventually life returned to some semblance of normality, until Bill and I began to experience slight electric shocks from various fittings. As it happened, Rosie had been married to an electrician and she asked him to check the house over. To our horror he declared the house to be electrically alive and switched off all but the most necessary equipment until we could contact the Electricity Board.

This was done, and the faulty wiring was corrected; at greater cost, of course. I had been greatly annoyed by Bill's cavalier attitude towards my complaints about the fridge. I had had some strong shocks from this particular item for quite some time but he had simply dismissed them.

Mark, Prue and I had always kept in touch with the latest family gossip and I was thrilled one year to be invited to join them on their holiday to Scotland. As a child, Prue and her sister, with their parents, had taken the train from Leeds to Inverness, then continued their journey by car to the very top of the land mass. Once there they stayed in the tiny hamlet of Polin Bay. This was the last inhabited cove on the west coast of Scotland and the original settlers were refugees from the Scottish Clearances. When Mark married Prue they continued to holiday as often as they could afford to do so. They had talked of this place often, and when I finally arrived I was immediately captivated by the isolated community. I was to hear later that Polin Bay was so far away that even many Scots themselves neither knew nor had heard of this place. I was fascinated to learn that three of the five families that lived there were direct descendants from the original settlers.

However, the hauntingly magical beauty could not fully compensate for the hardship these people must have experienced. I had my sketch book and paints with me, so while Mark and Prue went for their strenuous walks, I happily painted all day. Mark and I quickly settled into the comfortable relationship of our childhood and it was a great relief to be free from the strain of living with Bill. It was as well that I had such happy memories from that wonderful holiday to help me through what was to happen the following year.

Some time previously Mr Jacobs had had a heart attack, the curse of self employment, and inevitably he had to retire from the strain of such heavy responsibility. He sold the business to a small company in Newcastle and reassured the staff that our jobs would be secure as an agreement had been signed. There was no cause for concern. Finally the new people took over, and from the very beginning the atmosphere changed. Every other day a different man would stride through the shop, briefcase in hand, completely ignoring my polite greeting. As a supervisor and buyer of my department there were always certain matters to be discussed with management but I was never able to contact that level. I was simply dismissed with a mumbled excuse and a wave of the hand.

As time went by we began to realise they wanted to be rid of the older members of staff, and so the nightmare began. At first it was the little things which in themselves did not seem important. They began with the removal of my stool. This might not seem too alarming, but I had a great deal of handwriting to do, ordering of stock and customer enquiries etc. It was difficult to write standing up, so I used the shop circular mobile steps on which to perch awkwardly. When the men in grey suits realised what I was doing, the steps disappeared. All well and good, but these steps were used daily, as pictures and various items of stock hung high up on the walls.

Their next move, during the weekend, was to rearrange the whole shop. The pictures and paintings had gone, along with a large selection of very popular lines, simply to bring all items within our reach. I was deeply shocked at the length with which these people would go in order to drive me out and I was determined not to be beaten. However, as the weeks went by, I began to dread the days at work. The business had deteriorated into a shadow of its former self. All the colour, variety and interest had gone, leaving only a few dreary crafts with which to tempt the now dwindling custom.

My breaking point came, when one day, very publicly, I was soundly reprimanded for the severe drop in takings. I explained the reason why in an equally forcible manner, and two weeks later handed in my resignation.

Chapter Forty-nine

My fiftieth birthday fell in the year 1984 and I was beginning to feel that Orwell had a point in some of his predictions. In order not to slide into the thinking of 'the great unwashed' I jumped straight into menial shop work with very little money and long hours.

After the torment of the bullying that had forced me to leave a position where I had worked happily for over seven years, and the resultant chaos of my present work, I began to feel I was losing my grip on reality. So when I saw an advertisement for receptionist/telephonist I took a deep breath and applied. Within two weeks I found myself facing a seriously handsome young forty-something manager of the Volvo Car Showroom in Stockdale. It was a beautiful warm day in early September and the sun shone through the office window making the room rather uncomfortably warm. The interview was going quite well when suddenly, out of context, Mr Jamieson asked me my age.

I could feel myself blushing awkwardly as I muttered, "Fifty."

His reaction was of immediate astonishment, "Did you say fifty? Are you sure, Mrs Carter?" He enquired with a charming smile.

Needless to say, in spite of my advancing years and complete lack of experience, I got the job! And so once again I was thrown in at the deep end, with only a rudimentary training to cope with my first ever switchboard. Not only had I never seen a switchboard, I did not own a car and could not even drive. Being the new girl in any position, and at any age, is always difficult.

and from the very beginning I had to learn how to handle the teasing and ribald comments from a garage and showroom full of testosterone fuelled young men.

My main concern about my new job was the money I was to earn as a part-time employee. After talking it through with Sam I realised I would make a saving on travel expenses, because the showroom was on the outskirts of Stockdale and I could walk there if I so desired. Also the hourly rate of pay was higher than that I had received from Mr Jacobs, so all things considered there was not such a great difference between the two pay packets. After all these considerations had been cleared up, there was then the small worry about all the spare time I would have.

Once again Sam to the rescue. She had recently joined an evening class at the local school and suggested I do the same. The world was my oyster! Art, writing and philosophical classes were all booked up and eventually I was ready to go.

However, it took me quite some time to settle into the whims and fancies of a car showroom. It was, in essence, a bull ring. Beneath what seemed to be a breezy friendship between the salesmen, held together by their witty, sexual and highly amusing banter, lay the burning ambition and pressure of ever rising sales figures to be reached, and that could erupt into white hot fury at any moment.

As the precious years of my fifth decade slipped steadily by, the energy of these young men, full of enthusiasm and determination to live life to the full, helped to keep me young. They would talk to me about their troubles with children and their pride in personal achievements. I was involved in births, marriages and sadly two heartbreaking deaths. From the youngest trainee to the managers, who came and went with alarming frequency, they gave me their friendship and respect. I worked for the company for nearly eight years and I will always remember my time there with very deep affection.

Not long after I had come to grips with the antiquated switchboard the handsome Mr Jamieson told me I had been tested by a mystery shopper. This person had pretended to be a disgruntled customer and really put me through my paces. Apparently I handled the situation with text book perfection and the tape was to be used for training purposes throughout the company. I was thrilled by such flattery and it helped to lift my poor self-esteem which was particularly low at that point.

And now to my evening classes. It was through these innocent meetings that I met people from all walks of life, many of whom were able to advise me with my assorted problems. I also discovered the joys of coaching day trips and so my life opened up into two very different avenues, with the intellectual stimulus of the classes, combined with discovering the open road, all helping to broaden my horizons. This new life gave me the confidence to take two painting holidays on my own, which also led to meeting more people with fresh ideas.

Now that my Sundays were taken up with my magical coach trips it meant that my get together with the girls was over. I still managed to see them quite frequently, but it was part of my life I was sorry to lose.

Then I was sensing a strained atmosphere between Sam and Jack, and my grandson seemed to be unhappy. To ease the situation I began to take twelve year old Andy with me on my Sunday trips. What glorious fun we had together! I will always remember the day we went to that hauntingly beautiful place, Holy Island. Hand in hand we explored the fairytale castle then had our picnic on the beach. Here he splashed and paddled in the sea to his heart's content. It was so good to see him relaxed and happily laughing.

But one day, in 1988, Sam came crying to me that she had found a lump in her breast. My whole world collapsed, and the nightmare began. Appointments with doctors and hospitals, examinations and tests and then the final diagnosis.

All the confidence my new life had given me dissolved and I could feel myself breaking down. I would sit with my arms round my body, slowly rocking back and forth to a mantra of 'Dear God, don't let it be Sam, let it be me. Please God, let it be me. . .' over and over again. When catching sight of my perfect naked body I would break down into choking tears. Sleep became a distant visitor and I developed a dual personality.

The operation was done within days and I went to see Sam the next morning. She was sitting up in bed with Jack draped possessively round her shoulders. I felt something was wrong.

She greeted me with a smile. "Hello Mum. Well, it's all over, thank heavens. I insisted on a full mastectomy. They told me I was completely covered. So it's all gone and I am fine." Her eyes were shining with pain and fear and I could see the brittle self-control she was exerting to keep it all together. This other me chatted and laughed gaily for a while until she had to rest and I left her.

The healing process began with radiotherapy that drained the very life from her. I worried constantly that Jack was not looking after her properly and my mother's instinct told me something was wrong. By now I knew Jack well enough to know he would not take criticism of his judgement lightly and so my hands were tied.

Slowly, so slowly, my fragile child began to recover and the future was looking more positive, but I simply could not relax. I found myself watching her, watching her face and her movements, and I knew she was worrying about something, apart from hiding the pain she was still experiencing. Our two bodies had become as one and every twinge of pain she felt would stab through my body with such ferocity it was difficult to control.

Then out of the blue Robbie announced that he was to marry Rosie. It was to be a big affair in a small church with Rosie resplendent in the traditional meringue and Robbie in a dark suit. Rosie was very proud of her gypsy origins and at the reception the number of her family guests was almost tribal compared to Robbie's humble representation of a family. Sam and Lucy, with their husbands and children, and myself and Bill, sat quietly in a small corner while the celebrating began. Sitting next to Sam I was tight lipped and tense as I was aware of her rigid self-control.

The reception was held in a public house, and as the drinking began an announcement was made for the two mothers to go to the stage to receive their bouquets. Thunderous applause and cat calls broke out as Rosie's mother carefully disentangled herself from the numerous tables and chairs to walk gracefully to the stage. As this sort of thing was new to me I sheepishly followed behind.

On reaching the stage I was confronted by a deliriously happy Robbie swaying unsteadily on his feet while slurring his way through an embarrassingly exaggerated speech about the perfections of his new mother-in-law. A sharp nudge from his wife reminded him of his duties, and turning to me he said: "Oh, there you are, Mother, these are for you," and thrust a, by now, slightly wilting bunch of flowers into my arms. He then staggered back to the bosom of his new family.

I was tense and nervous about Sam during the whole affair, and could not wait to escape and return to the sanctuary of Tearo House. After a reasonable time we left, and Sam, Jack and Andy went back to Lucy's home, and apparently they all had a very merry party together.

I was so relieved that for just a few short hours Sam had had such a loving time with her sister and family. Lucy was to tell me that she had drunk too much and felt terribly ill the next day, but in retrospect she felt it was worth the discomfort.

Chapter Fifty

I tried to lose myself in my studying, and my coach journeys were always a great joy, but I could not rid myself of the sense of unease. Six months on from Sam's operation and the prognosis was looking good. I spent as much time with Sam as I could, and when I was with her I was always positive and optimistic. So much so, that one quiet summer's day I approached Bill and suggested that we took Sam out for a run while Jack was at work. He agreed, and we drove to a small 16th century village not far from Stockdale. It was a favourite place that, as a family, we often used to visit. We walked for a short distance by the fast flowing river, pottered in one or two quaint little shops, then went to the little café for a cup of tea and a scone. By now I was beginning to feel the strain of keeping the chatter on a breezy level, and we drove back to Tearo House.

Instinctively we gathered round the kitchen table to continue with our gossiping, when Sam asked for another cup of tea. And then Bill's temper erupted! My recall of the actual cause is a little vague. It was so trivial, as bad rows often are, but it was something to do with the way I was making the tea. Bill shouted at me, I retaliated and then Sam was screaming, "Stop it you two, for God's sake. Whenever are you going to stop. I can't take any more of this."

She ran out sobbing, and I found her in the bathroom breaking her heart. I could not bear her pain. I held her tightly, rocking back and forth until she calmed down, then we walked together to her home. On the way she asked me why did I stay with Bill, why didn't I leave him? It was so obvious the marriage was over.

I had been so shocked by Bill's appalling behaviour in front of our precious daughter when all I had tried to do was to support Sam with both our love. His petty-minded behaviour had ruined everything again. I had stayed with this man for so long, for two reasons: one, I could not afford to leave him, and two, I strongly believed it was better for my children for us to stay together. However, I now began to wonder.

Through one of my painting classes I had met and befriended a wonderful woman. Molly was a widow some ten years my senior and lived alone. She had one son who lived and worked in Scotland, but the distance did not in any way affect the bond between them. She lived in a delightful council flat a couple of miles from Tearo House and I used to imagine myself living in similar quarters.

On first meeting Molly I felt she was a little shy as she had a slow and precise manner of speech, but I was soon to discover that beneath her gentle demeanour there lay a will of iron and a razor-sharp sardonic wit that could reduce me to tears of laughter. She was born on the Isle of Wight but her family moved to the mainland and settled in Bournemouth. After the war, she studied at Bournemouth Art College, and was a trained and highly skilled painter, having a painting 'chosen but not hung' at the Royal Academy of Art. Molly had met and married a handsome young man from Poland, but her marriage proved to be as brutal as mine. In spite of this she was an incurable romantic, and if it had not been for her strength, support and encouragement I would never have taken the leap of faith I was to take some years later.

Not long after I had begun work at the garage, my beloved Beth died. Since Father's death I had visited her a couple of times and we had such fun together. When she died I was deeply saddened, and in order to share in her funeral, as it took place in Surrey, I sat quietly in the parish church in Stockdale. In spite of my experiences with the Presbyterian Church my faith still had meaning for me.

Beth had left me some money! I was now the possessor of £1000! I was deliriously happy and invested most of it in the Bradford and Bingley Building Society, but kept a little for holidays and small treats for Sam. Her improvement was happily reassuring and she bought herself a new car. A Volvo, as it happens. Not from the dealership where I worked, but from somebody Jack knew. And Jack always knew better, of course!

She loved this sleek, expensive vehicle as it had power assisted steering which helped with her driving. She could not wait to take me for a spin, and as we drove around we chatted and laughed with the sheer joy of life.

However, fate was lurking stealthily around Tearo House waiting to pounce on yet another unsuspecting victim. During the 1980s there had been two years of hot and exceptionally dry weather and all over the country buildings were cracking and moving to an alarming degree. Bill's insurance company inspected Grange Road, along with many other similar buildings, and were alarmed. They felt it was in danger of collapsing at some future date and wished to withdraw from insuring the property. They offered Bill £42,000 to buy him out. The whole situation was so unexpected that at first Bill was unsure as to what to do. So one day he told me of the situation, and explained that as he was over 70 years old the house would last long enough to ". . .see me out. It is the first time in my life I have ever had a bit of money, and I am damn well going to enjoy it." I quote.

I obviously misunderstood his meaning, when I said, "It would be wonderful to have £20,000 each in the bank."

There was a long pause.

"If you think I am going to give you any money when I have worked all my life to keep you in this house, you can think again. It is not going to happen."

I could hardly believe what I was hearing, and then I completely lost my temper. If he thought he was not going to share this windfall with me he simply did not know me.

"After forty years of drudgery and never ever any socialising together, always left with the children while you went out. Forty years of cleaning up after all the filthy animals you kept bringing home and leaving to me. Thirty years of working full-time keeping myself and contributing to the upkeep. Bringing up your children when there was not enough money to feed them. I will not let this go."

He listened to my furious tirade, then said quietly, "But you have money. Money that Beth left to you."

I was incandescent with fury. You see, Bill had a nasty little habit of steaming open my correspondence. After a few more colourful expletives from me, he said, "All right, I will give you a thousand pounds and then you can do what you damn well like."

I slammed out of the house and walked and walked until I began to calm down. I was fifty-six years old and had reached a crisis in my life. I simply had to do something. I talked it over with Molly and two weeks later I went to see a solicitor. I had consulted a solicitor about twenty years before, when I was employed by British Steel, and his advice was to stay put as I had no knowledge whatsoever of Bill's financial situation and I might end up with half of nothing. The outcome of this latest interview was that I could sue for a Legal Separation, whereby it cost less than a divorce but the money side was the same.

I had finally taken control of my life and felt better for having done so but was a little afraid of what the future may bring. I said nothing to the girls, as I could not face them at that point, instead I busied myself with work and painting with Molly. My case was to take at least three or four months so it was better to keep myself occupied.

By now Molly and I were attending life drawing classes and I found it challenging but very informative. Together we had entered one or two paintings into a small local art exhibition and we were both successful with our sales.

I talked for hours with Molly about my fears for the future. It would depend mainly on how much money I would be entitled to and quite how strong was my attachment to Tearo House. I could not help remembering how, one day in October the previous year, a young gypsy girl came begging at the front door. I crossed her palm with the obligatory pieces of silver, and as I was about to shut the door on her there was a crack of thunder and the heavens opened. There was nowhere for her to shelter so I asked her in. I explained I was preparing my lunch before going to work for the afternoon shift and took her down into the kitchen. She waited quietly in a corner and as I was eating my sandwich she suddenly spoke:

"Who is the woman in a pinafore who always looks after you?"

I was completely shocked and knew immediately that it was Mother she was referring to, which confirmed my overwhelming feeling I had when in the kitchen on my own. It was also the same with the bathroom. She then told me I would live to be an old woman and would walk with a stick but would be able to look after myself. I found this all very comforting and we went our separate ways. However, that made me realise quite how deeply attached I was to Tearo House.

Chapter Fifty-one

My uneasy fears about Sam now became horrifying reality. Jack's mother was a nurse at the big hospital, consequently Jack had extensive medical knowledge about all manner of illness and in particular breast implants! I just knew it! Ever since Sam had had the operation, Jack and his mother had worn the poor girl down with their insistence that everything would be all right and that she would feel so much better. The truth of it was that poor sensitive Jack could not bear to look at his wife's deformed body.

During the period when Sam was desperately trying to convince herself by reading up on every bit of medical advice about implantation, which was relatively new at that time, Bill's elder sister Jessie became ill. Jessie was a widow with one daughter and lived alone. Annie had died some years ago, and his other sister Francis lived in America where she worked as a pathologist in a large hospital.

I have observed, during my long life, that in all families there is always a member that holds the family together. In this case it is Lucy. As Jessie became more frail, Bill would do her shopping and run her about, but it was Lucy who cleaned her bungalow and, more importantly, found time to talk with her. When Jessie died, Lucy's grief was hard to bare and I was unable to console her in any way. I had never been able to reach out to Lucy in times of great stress, she simply locked herself away from life until she could face normality again.

Meanwhile, Sam finally succumbed to the pressure from her husband and a date was set for the operation. It was the nightmare of the cancer operation all over again and she went through hell. I went to see her the next day, and while I was there her doctor came in with her notes in his hand. He did not see me sitting behind the door and began to talk.

"My God Samantha you have been through the mill," then stopped abruptly when he saw me. He muttered an embarrassed apology but I asked him to continue, and after a few pertinent questions I was able to understand the agony she had suffered.

As I left the hospital where my child lay wracked with pain I thought of Jack and his mother and there was murder in my heart!

Her recovery took longer this time and, as with Lucy, I found it hard to bare. In spite of the pain she suffered, Sam seemed to be grateful that her pathetic husband now found her agreeable. I was beginning to wonder quite how strong Jack's influence was over her and felt as if I was slowly losing my children. After all, they were grown adults and making their own way in life. Robbie seemed to be very content with Rosie, although I suspect it was a highly charged marriage, and Lucy had Tom and her own children.

As I watched my two girls struggling with their lives, the tension between Bill and myself, although unspoken, was always there. Once again the strain of this peculiar life we led was beginning to tell on me, so with Molly's encouragement I booked another painting holiday. One of the boys at the garage suggested that I choose somewhere relatively close by, so that if I made friends we could stay in touch.

Oh, what amazing foresight that boy had shown! My holiday in the Lake District was to end my life in Tearo House forever.

Chapter Fifty-two

Two years later found me standing at Sam's grave in much the same way as when I first began this sorry tale. It was not long after Sam had died and my grief was draining the very life from my body. Without the love, understanding and compassion from the man by my side, I most certainly would have broken down. I left Stockdale and all that it held, to be with Adam, the man I met on that fateful holiday. He lived and worked in Lancashire which was now my home.

When I left Tearo House, at the age of fifty-eight years, I was reasonably content with the progression of Sam's health. Happily the distance between myself and Sam did not prevent us from seeing a great deal of each other. There had been an almost immediate rapport between Sam and Adam and it gladdened my heart to watch them together. Tragically this happy situation was not to last. Adam was the first to see the signs, as he had nursed his wife until she died some time before we had met. Sam's implant became infected and within seven months she was dead. As I had long suspected, Jack was incapable of facing Sam's illness and left Lucy and Tom to bare the brunt of looking after Sam.

The memories of that last nightmare year as Sam died slowly and painfully will stay with Lucy as long as she lives There were days of such unbearable pain, fear and despair that even today she cannot speak easily of them. Mere words cannot describe my feelings as I watched my child die. Suffice to say I was with her for the last four days and nights in the hospice. I developed a trance-like state of mind as I sat in a large chair by her bedside night and day. On the fourth night, as midnight approached, I was asked by a nurse to leave the room as a doctor was coming to see Sam. I remember hushed and urgent voices, as a tall man in a dark coat rushed past me and I was ushered out. Twenty minutes later I returned, and was told by a tearful nurse that Sam would be at peace soon. Sam died three and a half hours later.

Chapter Fifty-three

So, to continue with my story of the house that witnessed all these happenings. The house where Sam was born and the house where she and Mother will always live.

Bill lived on in Tearo House for nearly ten years, spending his money and watching the old place slipping into decay due to years of neglect. He obviously expected Lucy to look after him in every way, and she reluctantly complied. From what she tells me, his attitude towards her and Tom was that of sheer arrogance. However, he was her father and she carried out his orders promptly and efficiently with a loving care that he did not deserve. He rattled round the place in much the same way as he had when I was living there, only now he was quite open with all his lady friends. He entertained them in the kitchen, and on one occasion when Lucy called in with his heavy shopping, only to find the latest woman sitting in what she regarded as her kitchen, he actually ordered Lucy to make tea for them both.

His sexual activities slowed down with age and he spent more time at home with his many hobbies. A greater part of his day would be spent with Lucy in her home, generally causing havoc with his big hairy dogs and cigarette ash that spilt everywhere.

Ever since I had removed myself from the marriage, Lucy had taken on his laundry and was now coping with his cleaning, shopping and gardening. It is hard to believe he did not reward her financially for all that she did for him but he clung to his money like a drowning man. One day, when she was changing the sheets on his bed in the bedroom on the fourth floor, she found, to her horror, in a small cupboard in the bedroom, a manifestation of mice. Lucy contacted the council, the room was cleared and traps were laid. With the help of Tom and Michael, Bill's bed was brought down to the playroom. Once again the playroom was to have another occupant.

After that huge upheaval the fourth floor became unused, as Bill found no good reason to climb the flight of stairs. Lucy kept her eye on the three bedrooms, but the poor old house began to feel strangely unoccupied. The only part that had a welcoming feel was downstairs in the kitchen.

One Christmas Day Bill returned to Tearo House after spending the day with Lucy and her family. He poured himself a large tot of whisky, watched a little television then went to bed in the playroom. He woke the next day to find that thieves, believing the house to be empty, had stripped all the lead from the front bay sash window. Bill had the window repaired but it never really looked quite the same.

Each year the cracks worsened and still Lucy did her best to clean the house. As the carpets and furniture were all thirty years old there was very little she could do to eradicate an intangible feeling of decay that pervaded over the house and garden.

Meanwhile Lucy's life was being pulled apart in other directions.

When Sam died, her son Andy's life went to pieces. He mixed with the wrong crowd and drugs and drink became the norm. This started when there was a terrible row between Jack and Andy over the sale of their house, and Jack's true feelings for Andy rose to the fore. It was obvious he had tolerated Andy for Sam's sake but now she had gone the boy was a hindrance. In true Dickensian manner he threw Andy out while the boy was still grieving. Andy mixed with the wrong crowd and soon a pattern of drink and drugs became the norm. He lost his very good job at the council and was arrested when a drunken brawl got out of hand. He spent a week in the police cells before his case came to court, where he was sentenced to thirty hours community work. Through the whole nightmare period Lucy was by his side. Jack was nowhere to be seen.

At the age of twenty-one he inherited a large amount of money from Sam. This was enough to buy a very nice flat not far from

Lucy and we all helped to furnish his new home. Lucy added all the little touches that make such a difference and we hoped that finally he would settle down. He found another job and Lucy and Tom were always there providing a family background for him. But there was a wild streak in Andy, stemming from a childhood of rejection from Jack, and suddenly he sold everything, and with a few friends he left for Australia. This action broke Lucy's heart.

Time passed, and Bill was in his eighth decade. His health was beginning to cause concern as he was a heavy smoker and, I suppose, drank too much. He was not an alcoholic but he needed a drink every day. Lucy was now having to accompany him to his doctor's and hospital appointments. For her own peace of mind she began to call in every evening to make sure he had taken his night medication. During the colder weather she would make him a hot drink and fill numerous hot-water bottles. You may remember I have spoken of the icy temperatures in the old house many times!

However, his condition deteriorated and he was taken to hospital where he stayed for two weeks. He improved slightly and wanted to go home. Lucy organised a commode and oxygen for him in the playroom and he was glad to be back. With the help of Tom and Andy, somehow Lucy managed to run the two households in spite of them being twenty minutes walk away from each other.

Then one warm June evening, during Andy's watch, Lucy received a frantic phone call to get an ambulance. An ulcer had burst and Bill was vomiting blood from both ends. His body had simply lost control. Andy, not knowing whether Robbie was at home, rang Rosie as a back-up for Lucy. When Rosie arrived and found an unconscious Bill she could not cope and left. Lucy described the room as looking like that of a crime scene, with blood spatters everywhere as Bill had tried to get out of bed, fallen then collapsed. He was taken to hospital again, where all they could do was to make him comfortable.

Unfortunately Tom was working that night and Lucy had to leave the children on their own. Bill's admittance and attention all took a great deal of time and it was 3.00 a.m. in the morning before Lucy finally arrived home in a taxi. Bill had wanted to end his days in Tearo House, but his condition escalated rapidly and very sadly he died in hospital. By now Robbie was home and helped with the funeral arrangements. They all agreed it would be fitting for their father to leave for the church from the house, and so his coffin was brought to Tearo house. The night before the funeral they gathered together in the sitting room were Bill lay in his coffin.

Cans of beer and lager were opened. The atmosphere was almost convivial, but as the evening wore on the solemnity of the occasion began to overcome the happy reminiscing and chatter. One by one they left, until Lucy was finally alone in that large dark house. I can only imagine where her thoughts may have taken her. She had known this house all her life, being just a baby of two years old when Bill and I moved to Grange Road. Memories of her childhood, all her loves and hates, all her hopes and regrets, and the unbearable loss of her sister, all were with her that long night she sat in Bill's old armchair in the kitchen with only her faithful dog by her side.

But she could not rest. Some primaeval urge caused her to check time and again that Bill was still in his coffin. She imagined him to be wandering silent and ghost-like through the musty empty rooms. She felt he was looking for something, of what she could not be sure. When I saw her the next day, I was shocked to see how dreadful she looked. The last few agonising years of loss, exhaustion and pain were etched into her very soul As I looked into those weary eyes, devoid of life and hope, I wondered whether I would ever hear that gay infectious laughter again.

Chapter Fifty-four

LUCY'S STORY

When I divorced Bill in order to marry Adam, part of my settlement was a half share in Tearo House. When Bill died, Lucy inherited his half share of the house. So what else could I do but to give her my share. I hoped she would sell the house and for the first time in her life have money in her pocket. I really felt the poor old house had come to his end, as it was obvious so much work was needed to be done. However, I had not accounted for the strength, determination and sheer bloody-mindedness of my young daughter.

It was an almost impossible project for one girl to take on, and Tom had his misgivings. I suspect he was not one hundred per cent behind her but, in spite of his feelings, Lucy went ahead with the whole enormous procedure. To begin with she contacted an estate agent and surveyor. She had to know how much to expect from the sale of their undoubtedly well-appointed ex-council house before she made a move. The figure was acceptable and she then contacted the surveyor about Tearo House. He had misgivings and had the house monitored for two months. This was to make sure the alarming cracks in the landings had only been caused by old settlement. During this worrying period Lucy began to methodically empty the house of thirty years of junk that Bill and I had collected. She was ruthless, everything had to go, this was a completely new start.

However, one morning when she took her dog for his walk, she passed by the house and a quick glance told her something was wrong. On her return she realised it was the curtains. She was absolutely certain they had been open when she had left the house two days previously. Her heart stopped. Somebody was in there. She called the police and a young police girl arrived. Together they cautiously searched the house and loft, and on closer inspection of the grounds human excrement was found in the bushes near the drive. Obviously squatters were taking over as they had slept in the sitting room and stolen quite a number of items. The police warned Lucy to be careful and not to enter on her own, but the next time Lucy called at the house all signs of them had gone.

The squatters returned, but another police inspection served its purpose in frightening them off never to return. Nevertheless, Lucy was beginning to feel unnerved as well as impatient. Her house had been sold by now and she was itching to get started, so a few sharp words were needed with the surveyor. She had taken out a six month rental lease on a house not far from Grange Road, and it was a race against time.

To my horror, the first clearance began with the trees. According to the surveyor the roots of so many trees were undermining the foundations of the house. I felt it was rather a rash move. I found it difficult to hold back my tears when I knew my beloved old willow tree, whose three hundred year old roots had lived there for so long, had to go. This magnificent specimen had been a living, breathing physical presence all through my childhood and married life. My brothers and I had climbed, played and dreamed our dreams amongst its huge branches and sweet smelling protective foliage. The tree dominated our lives, garden and house. Its beauty could be seen from every window at the back of the building. Through the long years of war and deprivation it gave us a sense of security, and its support was also there through my troubled adulthood.

Sadly my three children did not find the joy and love that my brothers and I had for the old willow, but Lucy did tell me that she once climbed it. When speaking of my sadness to her I was told "It was very old and dangerous, and badly diseased, so it had to come down, Mother."

Some readers may find my emotional attachment to a tree rather strange, but this particular tree was so very much part of the house that when it had gone a small part of the house was lost as well. Happily one small apple tree in the back garden and large sycamore tree in the drive were allowed to remain. Fortunately I was not to witness the destruction of my childhood memories as Adam and I did not visit the house until a greater part of the rebuilding had taken place.

Lucy took us through the front door into a world of scaffolding and whistling cheerful workmen. We crunched our way through the hall, taking one fearful glance into the decimated sitting room before scrambling under the scaffolding down the stairs to the kitchen. I gazed in utter disbelief at the naked brick walls of what had been my cosy kitchen. From floor to ceiling it was stripped bare as was the rest of the house. All signs of the improvement Bill had made, the lino tiled floor to the boarded ceiling, all were gone. Lucy and her merry gang of workmen had been ruthless in their rebuilding of this one hundred and ten year old structure; for at this point that was all it was.

A twenty-six foot steel beam had been erected beneath the top landing running though the back bedroom to the gable end. This drastic repair had been absolutely necessary as the house was on the point of collapse.

As we left the house that day I found it almost impossible to imagine that this shell of a building would ever be habitable again. However, Lucy had some important shopping to do. Two new fireplaces were needed and a bespoke front door and porch. Lucy was working on a tight budget, but luckily she had a nose for a bargain. It was by sheer chance that she found a small advert in the local paper for a master joiner. Tom and she eventually found his business in the old part of the town down by the river and were thrilled with the quality of his work. He, in turn, showed a great interest in the old house and was pleased to carry out the work that was required. Lucy got to know old George quite well, as he was a conscientious and diligent worker.

George's love for his work found him, one early spring evening, working alone in the house. As the light began to fade, he became aware of somebody watching him. George was a no nonsense, down to earth man and tried to ignore the feeling, but the sensation became so powerful he almost fled from the building. When he next saw Lucy he told her there was definitely a presence in the house and he would not work there alone ever again. Strangely, after George's confession, Terry, a young outgoing confident plasterer, finally admitted that he too had

j

experienced the same chilling sensation. Lucy's cheeky grin and engaging wit had endeared her to the workmen and they were deeply concerned for her welfare. But her positivity and determination to live in this house overcame their cautionary warnings.

Chapter Fifty-five

Her next large purchase was to be the fireplaces. This shopping expedition was to prove sadly unsuccessful. To begin with, fireplaces themselves are not so easy to find, as this is the 21st century where the goggle box god is worshipped and warmth comes from a boiler hidden in the kitchen. Lucy was beginning to panic as time was running out.

One day she and Tom were pottering in a small arcade of shops the other side of the cemetery. This street was squashed in between a Methodist church and a very popular pub. Originally the shops had been privately owned and highly exclusive. The passing of time had brought a more mundane type of business, one of which was a gas showroom. As a last resort, Tom and Lucy entered and wandered aimlessly around, all hope fading. They were just about to leave when a sales man approached. As luck would have it, the company had two fireplaces in stock that were waiting to be returned to the wholesaler. Incredibly they could have been tailor-made for Tearo House and Lucy could not believe her luck. Which indeed became better still, as they bought the gas fires as well, which with the discount came to nearly half the full price.

The work was progressing quite well but had overrun the six month lease. Fortunately the estate agent was sympathetic to Lucy's project and allowed her another month's leeway. The plastering was finished as was the rewiring and central heating. Double glazed windows were fitted, along with a new bath, shower, lavatory and wash hand basin. A wood floor was laid in the bathroom and all inside doors rehung. Damaged skirting and floorboards were repaired. The cornice in the sitting room had been damaged and the joiner very skilfully repaired the delicate plastering. Tom and Lucy were thrilled with his artistry. The ceiling rose in this room, for some strange reason, was much smaller than that of the playroom. That one was large and highly decorative, but with time had deteriorated. During the 1960s Bill had boarded over the ceiling and Lucy wanted to display this highly ornate ceiling rose. On close inspection the joiner explained that it would be extremely costly to repair the work, so Lucy had, in this case, to acknowledge the joiner's experience and agree to the boarding.

Another month passed and the sympathetic estate agent became a little less sympathetic but did agree to just one month more. The race was on! This mammoth undertaking had the overtones of a Grand Designs project, but without the eye-watering amounts of money and the slightly pretentious attitude of the owner. Lucy's whole aim was to preserve rather than create. Bearing in mind she was having to oversee the whole project more or less on her own, as Tom, through no fault of his own, could not always be there. Lucy was having to deal with the north east workmen, who at first resented having to take instructions from a slip of a girl.

There was one last important decision to be made and that was the kitchen. The most important room in the house. As Lucy had known Tearo House from childhood, she was keen to make alterations and put her own mark on the house. As her two teenage children were living with them, they too had ideas about decor and such. Wickes' Kitchen Designer was called in but he found the room challenging.

There was also a problem with the large square bay window, as it was not a standard size. There was one harrowing day when Lucy found herself surrounded in the kitchen by the surveyor, plumber, plasterer, builder and the kitchen man all wanting answers. With her head in a whirl, she agreed rather hastily to a particular plan that was to prove rather restrictive when they were finally in residence.

The clock was ticking with still so much to do. A special type of slate tile had to be chosen for the kitchen floor, and curtain rail and blinds were to be fitted on all windows. Last but not least, the entire house had to be carpeted. Also the front garden and drive had to be completely landscaped, but that would have to wait.

Amazingly, with only one day to spare of their allotted time, this little family were sleeping in their beds in Tearo House. This old house, although still the same, was completely rejuvenated. From his foundations to his roof he was renewed, strengthened and strong, and ready for another 100 years. As the family moved in he smiled contentedly in the warm spring sunshine, for once again children's laughter could be heard. Oh, how happy was he! Slowly the family settled down to their daily lives. Tom as a heavy goods driver, Sarah as a histology secretary and Michael as a trainee manager with the same company as his father. And finally Lucy was able to expand her family of dogs.

The children, coming from a charming but modest social house, revelled in the space and grandeur of their new home. One day Lucy found Michael moving slowly from floor to floor. Not wishing to intrude, she caustically enquired whether he was looking for something, "No, thank you, Mother, just wandering," came the reply with a dreamy look in his eye, "just wandering."

Unfortunately their happiness was to be short-lived as only a few months later Tom was made redundant. This was a terrible blow because Tom had been with the company for well over twenty years and was happy in his work. For a while Tom and Lucy were desperately worried as there was still much to do in the house, notwithstanding the gardens.

Fortunately, Tom's reputation stood him in good stead and as he was given a month's notice he was soon able to find another position. His redundancy money was a substantial amount which enabled them to have all the gardens, back and front, landscaped. It was not until this enormous task was completed that Adam and I went to view my reborn Tearo House.

Chapter Fifty-six

By this time Adam and I were in our 70s and had been married for over twelve years We had just completed our fourth house move to a small market town twelve miles from Stockdale.

It had taken Lucy many years to accept Adam, but slowly with time, a deep affection grew between them. My life with Adam had been one glorious, romantic, exciting whirl, living every moment to the full. He was the man who pulled me back from near insanity after Sam's death and it was with this man I came alive.

Before we met, Adam's life had been that of which I had only dreamt. He was born in the Lake District, and as a shy 16 year old went to Sheffield where his older brother, George, was studying at the university. George kept an eye on him until he was earning enough money to keep himself as a trained gent's barber.

So there I was. Lucy had requested that I did not see the house until the gardens had been landscaped and now that time had come. With Adam by my side I gazed in complete astonishment at what had at one time been the front garden of 23 Grange Road. A great swathe of delicately coloured block paving swept away from me down to the front door and across to the double garage. Not a trace of the old garden existed apart from one broad leafed tree on my right. Huge double wrought-iron gates protected the property from the street. Large tubs of coloured shrubs were attractively placed around the large bay window and the small iron gate between the house and the garage that led to the back garden. Climbing wisteria was slowly establishing itself on a trellis between the front door and the window. In the top corner, to my left, a large semi-circle of rich green lawn held a circular bed in which a delicate weeping willow swayed gently in a small breeze. It took me all of five minutes to fully absorb this complete transformation, and momentarily I felt a fleeting flicker of regret at the loss of that tree-shaded lawn and flower beds which I knew so intimately. This was modernism at its best and as they were a three car family it had been well planned. Lucy and Tom hovered happily round me laughing at my incredulity, but as I approached the front door I began to wonder at what I may find.

It was a beautiful front door, solid and reassuring, and the freshly painted exterior gleamed proudly in the soft sunshine. Holding my breath I carefully pushed it open to reveal my long lost porch. Immediately I stepped back in time and Mother was by my side. I was four years old and Mother was opening the front door to a shivering postman. It was Christmas Eve and the snow was thick and deep and crunched loudly beneath his heavy boots. Happy Christmas greetings were exchanged as Mother received the long awaited parcel. It was meticulously wrapped in brown paper and tied up with string. The parcel crinkled invitingly in Mother's hands promising untold joy. My excitement was so intense I was sick on the spot.

Back to the present, and opening the inner door I was greeted by a lifelong dream. Wall to wall hard wearing dark cream coloured carpet began from the kitchen door up the stairs through the hall. It then swept up the gracious middle staircase onto the large bathroom landing, and finally up the third flight of stairs to the square bedroom landing. It was quite breathtaking. All I had ever known were various lengths of different coloured carpet.

Lucy and Tom were watching me, anxiously waiting for my approval. And now to the sitting room! Speechlessly I gazed around at this so familiar elegant room that now had an air of subtle opulence. Two dark green leather chesterfields provided the seating, while green diaphanous curtaining swept from ceiling to floor, giving a romantically extravagant look which was reflected in the large Laura Ashley square rug placed in the middle of the fitted carpet. A television set stood in one alcove, while in the window alcove a Victorian occasional table held a contemporary table lamp which, with its twin in the opposite corner, provided the light source. A delicate chandelier hung from the large rose in the ceiling to give a more general light. A large antique chest stood in the bay window, with a colourful throw folded neatly across the right side and a couple of hard backed books placed on the left. Beside the chest was a tall plant with glossy rounded dark green leaves. A smaller plant was on the table in the alcove, while on the floor rested a floor standing bookcase made by my father. Carefully chosen ornaments graced the Victorian stone fireplace and tasteful paintings hung on the walls. Cushions and throws added a vivid splash of colour to complete the look of tasteful simplicity.

As I turned to Lucy she laughed at my bewilderment and explained everything had been done on a shoestring. She had haunted salesrooms, antique shops and charity shops for months and had found some wonderful bargains. Feeling almost dazed with the transformation I moved into the playroom. Once again I gasped.

Sunlight streamed through two sash windows from which curtains the colour of golden butter hung. The furnishings reflected the sun in the warm colour of the polished oak bureau and wooden bookcase. The glowing colour of the pine wood fireplace enhanced the mustard rug in the middle of the room, while contemporary touches in the shape of standard lamps, ornaments and paintings were arranged in the appropriate positions. A large pine framed mirror hung over the mantelshelf while two comfortable sofas from their old home completed this sun-filled intimate room.

The ghosts of so many people who had come and gone through this room washed over me, but my sombre mood lightened when Lucy explained that the large footstool in front of the window that looked down onto the garden was where her two dogs sat when on 'squirrel patrol'.

Moving up the staircase to the bathroom landing, there was a free-standing tall boy stood in the alcove while in the other corner a cream covered tub chair invited one to relax and look across the garden to the hills beyond. Hanging over the tall boy was a charcoal drawing of a reclining nude. One of my best, I thought! However, this peaceful corner did not prepare me for what I was about to discover. Here the old and new lived together in perfec harmony. The silky smooth plastered walls were tiled half way, instantly declaring that the room was to be used for personal toilette only. The opening of Christmas presents and girlie hairdo parties simply would not happen in this cleverly designed room. A new bath was in the same position as the old one had been, and to keep the cost down the shower was over the bath. Next to the window stood an ultra modern water closet, and between there and the fireplace stood a large clothes basket. The delicate little fireplace had been painted in a special non-rust paint and replacing the corals a large china flowerpot held a glossy rubber plant. Above the mantelshelf, on which stood candles of various sizes and a coloured glass bottle, a large round black-rimmed clock with tall black numbers hung. This was to help the family with the early morning rush to work, Lucy laughingly explained. Standing against the long wall was the very latest in wash hand basins. It was a circular glass bowl standing on a short chrome pedestal. Bowl and pedestal stood on a square black base which, in turn, was supported by four chrome legs with shelving on either side. Above the basin was a pretty oval mirror. This whole fitting was so unexpected, but helped to prevent overdoing the Victorian look. Standing next to the basin was a solid heavy wood towel stand. A new wood floor had been laid.

Standing next to the bath was a cream leather easy chair. This was as surprising as the wash hand basin. The futuristic curved shape, supported on chrome legs, perfectly reflected the simple lines of the basin. Lucy had exceeded herself in redesigning this room when working on such a tight budget.

I moved slowly up the carpeted staircase to the final landing, to be greeted yet again with simple elegance. A nursing chair that Sam had had recovered fitted well in this space and, with a large table lamp standing on a small wood stool made by my father, the picture was completed.

I slowly inspected the bedrooms, making the appropriate comments, while all my ghosts with their tears and laughter continued to follow me around.

I then had to prepare myself for what I was about to find. The kitchen! So much had happened in this room, both in childhood and old age, I wondered how I may react. I pushed open the door and gasped. Lucy had worked her magic again. Two rows of gleaming up-to-date wall cupboards and kitchen worktops stretched nearly to the fireplace. Inside the new UPVC square window stood the washing machine, sink and drainer and another cupboard. A smart new wood burner fitted in the space where the coal fire had once been, and a new floor had been laid in an easy clean slate tile. I was greatly relieved to see my old clothes rack hanging from the ceiling.

In the centre of all this shining modernity was Lucy's pride and joy: my old kitchen table that Bill, in his declining years, had stripped and polished until it gleamed. Lucy really loved this table, with its copious drawer and sturdy legs. She happily overlooked the fact that in this new arrangement it practically filled the room. For the last fifty years the table had always rested against the long wall but now there was nowhere else for it to stand. I continued to gaze, completely lost for words.

What could I say? Old kitchen gone?

The room I had known was undoubtedly shabby, but the basic shape and position had always evoked a country kitchen feeling. But this room meant business. The business of cooking and eating, and even sharing a bottle of wine or two. There remained only one corner that bore any resemblance to that cosy old room I remembered, and that was a chair in the corner by the fireplace.

Lucy and Tom hovered, anxiously waiting for my approval, and all I could say was, "It is absolutely astonishing, darling. Completely breathtaking. I never ever imagined it could look so wonderful." They beamed with delight at my comments and began to tell me of all the mishaps they had encountered during the restorations.

We sat together round the table while Lucy busied herself preparing a light lunch in her sparkling easy-clean kitchen. I almost envied her the newness of everything. However cosy my old kitchen may have been I would have given anything for those wonderful units and the self-clean oven! Eventually the children came home from school and I was relieved to see that this was still the room where everybody gathered. Lucy's imagination and genuine love for the house had brought it into the 21st century while still retaining its Victorian origins. Fortunately Lucy had had the wherewithal to secure the walls while fulfilling its obvious potential.

Mother and I had always been aware of the possibilities this gracious house held but had been thwarted by poverty. However to his credit, Bill had the foresight and ability to make the greatest improvement to the property by closing down the scullery. He then enlarged the kitchen by inserting a 3x7 foot bay widow. I remember that time so well! Three small children to feed, keep clean and safe with no running water and half the kitchen open to the elements!

And so, once again, Tearo House was smiling as it was about to experience the lives of yet another generation unfold within its solid and welcoming walls.

Chapter Fifty-seven

And there we are!

Lucy and Tom in their new home with two teenage children, three dogs, one aged rabbit, a flourishing wildlife and bird table. Adam and I, now in our early 70s were living nearby and still busy with exhibiting our paintings on a yearly basis in the North York Moors Visitor Centre. Robbie and Rosie were living in Spain, and since his father's death Robbie's attitude toward me had changed completely. He was now warm and loving, and Adam and I had spent some hilarious holidays with them in their amazing villa.

Sadly, even though Robbie was in his 50s, with all the ailments that befall a deep sea diver, he was constantly seeking employment in life-threatening war torn countries. The more dangerous the work, the higher the remuneration. This was needed to maintain the extremely lavish lifestyle that Rosie and he enjoyed. And so I have spent my long life praying for his safe return from each trip.

Time passed, and Sarah and Michael grew to the age where mother nature urged them to seek a partner. All well and good, but why oh why do teenage hormones cause people to make such disastrous choices. Michael, even though he was younger than Sarah, was the first to make the leap from boyhood to unwanted fatherhood. His gentle innocence was destroyed by a hard drinking world-wise girl. When she declared that Michael was the father of her second pregnancy, Lucy was distraught.

A great deal of anger, pain and heartache ensued between the two families until one New Year's Eve my first great-grandchild was born. I was almost bemused with wonderment at this joyous birth, and Lucy completely lost her heart to her first grandchild. A girl, named Evie. The mother was a hairdresser and Michael was only just beginning to earn, so where else could this little family go but to Tearo House.

I swear I could almost feel the old house smiling at the thought of another baby within his walls. The house was bursting at the seams with prams and cots and clutter, and confusion and laughter and irritation. But, with Lucy at the helm, there was some semblance of order. One evening, when Michael was working a night shift and the mother out and about, Lucy was feeding the, by now, six months old Evie in her high chair in the kitchen. Sarah, having returned from her work at the hospital, was sitting in the corner by the fire. The high chair was on her left and Lucy on the other side. The three of them were facing down the kitchen to the open door and a dark space at the bottom of the stairs.

It was a happy scene; mother, daughter and granddaughter all together. Sarah and Lucy smiled as they watched the baby girl intent on making as much noise as she could with her spoon. Lucy continued to spoon feed her. Suddenly, baby Evie looked directly down the room to the open door. She stared intently at the dark space, her arms slowly dropping onto the tray of her chair. She continued to stare. Lucy and Sarah froze! "What on earth is she looking at?" Sarah whispered to her mother.

"I don't know," came the reply, "but there is definitely something there," Lucy finished.

As they watched Evie a slow smile of recognition spread across her face. One arm slowly raised in a hesitant wave directly at the dark space. She continued to wave while smiling happily at the open door, then as swiftly as it had begun it changed. Her bottom lip quivered, her face crumpled and tears began to flow.

Lucy and Sarah were shocked to the core, and as Lucy comforted the distressed child she knew that something quite extraordinary had happened that evening. When Lucy and I discussed the incident later on I instinctively felt that it was Sam trying to communicate with her still grieving sister.

Six years later, Sam appeared to her own grandson! I will tell of this when the time is right.

Sarah, intelligent, gregarious, ambitious and emotional had

two unhappy affairs before choosing her Prince Charming. Eight years older than Sarah, divorced with two children and an inherited disability that affected his nervous system, was Nigel! Sarah desperately wanted children but sadly it was not to be. Every single avenue was explored but without success. As a last resort they went through the emotional roller coaster of adoption.

After many months of nerve-wracking testing and interviewing they were finally awarded a two-year-old girl called Susie.

Sarah was ecstatically happy with her brown eyed, shy little girl and even Nigel fell for her charms. Susie had everything a girl could desire. A secure and loving home background and her material needs were supplied in abundance. However, this overwhelming spoiling made for some undesirable behaviour traits.

In almost shocking contrast to Susie's perfect childhood, Evie's was desperately sad. Her parents eventually bought a house, with help from Lucy and Tom, and for a few short years Evie was to live with her natural parents.

Michael adored his baby daughter and with Lucy's help became a hands-on father.

Sadly this volatile relationship did not last and the unhappy couple parted. Evie was taken by her mother to live with Evie's grandmother and Michael returned to Tearo House to lick his wounds and recover from a broken heart. He threw himself into work and amazingly, within a couple of years, he had regained ownership of his house.

However, there was one place where Evie was to find consistency, security, warmth and love. That was with Lucy, her three dogs and Tearo House. It was only within these four walls she could relax and become the bright and loving little girl she really was. Lucy's love of all living creatures had instilled in the child the same deep interest and they were to share this joy for many years to come. Long walks together, come rain or shine, with Lucy's three dogs, became a necessary part of Evie's young life.

In spite of Lucy's mature years she had the imagination and ability to play with Evie at her own level. I always thought Lucy would take to the stage as my father's first cousin was Sir Johnston Forbes Robertson. Later on it was Evie who was to prove that acting came naturally to her, and during their long walks Evie would play out all that she experienced in her mother's chaotic home life.

I am well aware that if true love exists in the home, however humble it may be, that is all that matters, but this sprawling old house with its dark corners, large rooms and garden had a distinct advantage over all the other houses Evie was to know so intimately. Tearo House just loved to be dressed up, so when Halloween came along he revelled in Lucy's abundance of spiders, witches, cobwebs and broomsticks. Evie adored Christmas too, and this was the time when the house came into his own. There had always been a special atmosphere at this time, from the coloured paper chains and threadbare Christmas tree of my war time childhood, to the exciting freshly cut tree of my children's early years. Holly and ivy, balloons and tinsel would complete my acknowledgement to the season. But when Lucy's time came the house took on a truly Dickensian persona! A very tall tree would stand in the large bay window, the curtains draped elegantly on either side. With garlands, candles and soft lights the sitting room looked like a scene from a Christmas card. The hall, staircases and landings were equally tastefully dressed and it was pure magic! Evie just loved the colour, warmth and air of expectancy that pervaded the old house and was fully appreciative of all the work involved.

As Evie progressed through her schooling years, Lucy and I became aware that a very bright and intelligent child was emerging in spite of the tumultuous and emotional life she led. One bright sunny morning, after Evie had spent the day before at Tearo House, Lucy was surprised on opening the front door to find quite a large group of animated people gathering in the front garden. It transpired that Evie had the night before attached a notice onto the big iron gates. It read thus:

FARM ANIMALS ON DISPLAY
HOMEMADE SCONES & TEA PROVIDED
Admission £1.00

A deeply embarrassed Lucy did her best to pacify a, by now, rather irate group that it was her granddaughter's wishful thinking that had prompted this action. Eventually they understood and left quite happily. But when, a few weeks later, Lucy had to pacify a rather belligerent gentleman knocking on the front door demanding to see the Border terrier puppies that were for sale, she knew she had to put a stop to her granddaughter's antics.

As Lucy told me of these exploits she could not disguise the pride she felt, for although Evie was only six years old these posters had been written in such a manner that showed a maturity beyond her years.

Evie was approaching her seventh birthday and she began to long for a dog of her own. Michael was still living with his parents and consequently Evie was spending more time at Tearo House. Lucy already had three dogs and, as all you dog owners and lovers of these precious pooches well know, the cost of their upkeep is considerable. Sacrifices have to be made and in Lucy's case they were many.

A family meeting was held and the outcome was that Michael would cover the cost of the puppy and all the necessary injections. He would also take out an insurance on the dog's health and pay any vet's bills that may occur. Tom, in order to please his son, agreed to cover the cost of feeding the animal.

Lucy was well aware of all the little irritations that another animal in the house could cause, apart from all the work that inevitably would fall on her shoulders, but reluctantly she agreed and the search was on for a puppy for Evie.

However, cracks were appearing in Tom and Lucy's marriage. Cracks that may have begun way back, who is to know, but the strain of Michael's domestic breakdown and the upkeep of her dogs had all taken a toll on their relationship. On top of which Sarah had left home to live with her partner in a village some miles from Stockdale.

Sarah moving out had been a terrible blow for Lucy, as mother and daughter were so close, in much the same way Samantha, Lucy and I were, and somehow Lucy was hoping Sarah would not move quite so far afield.

Chapter Fifty-eight

Evie's favourite film was Walt Disney's 'The Lady and the Tramp' so of course her new puppy had to be a Cavalier King Charles Spaniel.

Michael and Evie waited patiently for a few weeks, then a litter of puppies was advertised in the local paper and a puppy was chosen.

Molly was the most adorable bunch of cuddle I have ever seen, and I have handled a great number of puppies in my time! Her colouring was liver and white, soft and silky to the touch and she had the happiest of dispositions. So life with Molly began. Lucy put aside her worries and it was not until eight years later her very worst fears were realised.

In the meantime, these four dogs became Lucy's life. Bringing her love, joy and heartache. She became well known locally walking with her granddaughter and four distinctive dogs. Evie was showing an intelligent interest in her grandmother's expertise and was quick to pick up the ins and outs of animal welfare. Lucy was constantly giving advice to a worried owner about their ailing animal, and she was glad to help. She began to be known amongst her dog walking friends as the dog equivalent of the 'horse whisperer'.

When Millie died, having been the first Border terrier Lucy had owned, Lucy found herself overwhelmed with such genuine understanding from a wide variety of people. From sweet little old ladies, eyes brimming with sadness, to burly retired lorry drivers. In one case, the most unlikely hard bitten ex-council worker silently slipped into her hand a poem he had written of such tenderness that Lucy very nearly broke down.

When Lucy's neighbour's dog attacked little Nell, who then contracted diabetes, Lucy's caring and nursing of the animal knew no bounds. Sometimes I found her devotion and self sacrifice for Nell hard to watch. During the last two years of the little dog's life Lucy bought her, with Sarah's help online, a dog buggy. Now perhaps in the more enlightened south this might not have caused such a stir but in the north she practically stopped the traffic.

One year Tom, Lucy, Evie and the dogs took a five day caravanning holiday on a campsite near York. When spending the day in the ancient city Lucy, Evie and the buggy found themselves to be the centre of attention. Time and again they were asked by a jovial tourist if they could take a photograph of the little group. At first Tom was amused, but after a while 'man like' he became irritated by their popularity. Seven-year-old Evie thoroughly enjoyed the attention and posed like a natural.

Back in Stockdale, Lucy was not only admired for her dedication to the sick animal but also faced the abuse that was thrown at her. Quite often I worried for her safety as illiterate and drunken youths could become rather menacing in their fatuous comments.

Her popularity spread and even strangers would approach her telling of an acquaintance who had spoken of the 'pram woman' and asking to see the star of the show, little Nell.

When Nell died Lucy went out of her way to avoid all her well meaning friends as she knew she would find it impossible to cope with their genuine sympathy. It was many months before she found another puppy, but when Nancy came into her life Lucy's terrible grief became easier. This new puppy was the most mischievous, intelligent and, at times, promiscuous of animals I have ever known. She touched everyone's heart and became as popular as Lucy herself. I will be eternally grateful to this little minx for making my daughter laugh again.

However, as Lucy had feared, eight years ago Molly became extremely ill and needed an operation. The cost was astronomical and tensions grew between Tom and Lucy. Once again, Lucy's friends rallied round, and one dear soul even offered a financial loan to help with the cost. Lucy is a very private person and has difficulty in finding the right words with which to express her gratitude.

Ironically it is becoming increasingly clear that Lucy's life is running a similar course to that of myself and my mother. For entirely different reasons we all saw Tearo House to be the answer to our happiness. For Mother it was to prevent separation from Father whom she still loved. In my case it was to fill the aching gap in my life when my parents moved south, and for Lucy it was to help her while grieving for her father. Once again, in all three cases, the marriage broke down. Mother and Lucy remained with their spouses through a weary resignation of the situation, but the love had gone. However Tearo House must take his share of the blame in these broken relationships. The house is arranged in such a manner that two people can easily live apart. In my case this separation led to breakdown of the marriage. So I left!

Eventually Michael redecorated his house throughout and his parents and I were extremely proud of his achievements. With time, as Evie grew older, father and daughter were to spend many happy hours in each other's company. They found a common interest in food and together produced well cooked meals. Evie learnt to live happily in her father's home at weekends and with her mother and stepfather during the week.

As previously mentioned, Evie was seven years old when Susie came to be my second great-granddaughter through Sarah and Nigel's adoption of her. She came from a drug-ridden mother as a two year old and was a shy and nervous child at first. With time and overwhelming love from both Sarah and Nigel the little girl flourished, Sarah was a deeply caring girl and after all those years of longing and hoping for a child, Susie transformed her life.

Susie is now seven years old and happily settled in a small and caring village school. However, Sarah has her hands full as Nigel has an inherited illness rather like Parkinson's disease. This illness affects his nervous system and cannot be cured. In spite of poor health Nigel continues to work. This causes extreme tiredness, leaving Sarah to cope with her work at the hospital, her daughter and a sick partner. Despite her work load she remains bright and cheerful. Sarah and Nigel's lives revolve round Susie and as she is a happy and confident little girl they are content.

Then there is Andy. My restless wandering first grandchild. When he was born we all lived in Tearo House. He was a confirmed bachelor until, at the age of forty-two, he and his Italian beauty presented me with my third great-grandchild, William. Andy was a very hands-on father and the little family moved to Stockdale. He was feeling the pull of Tearo House in much the same way as Lucy and I, but, of course, situations had changed.

Unfortunately he was unable to find work locally and eventually they returned to Australia. While they were here I was privileged to watch the blossoming of an impressive artistic talent. At the age of twenty-four months I watched William at his painting desk and it was a revelation. His concentration was intense. His brush strokes were thoughtful, planned and deliberate. Every stroke had a position in the montage he was creating, which had a specific colour scheme, shape and form. It was spring time when I watched him painting and his mother told me he particularly loved daffodils. His painting of a daffodil would have impressed Picasso and it is still hanging on my wall.

As I watched that baby boy with his slow thoughtful brush strokes, I realised with a thrill that he was special! He is four years old now and very much a tomboy, so I hope his natural instinct is encouraged by his teachers. Andy is happily settled in Australia with a good job, a house and a wonderful life style. My only sadness is that William will grow into manhood never knowing his great-grandmother.

Robbie and Rosie never had children. Rosie had two children from her first marriage and was happy enough with them, and Robbie was unable to have children. This was caused by a terrible accident when diving with the Royal Navy in Ireland. He did two trips to a small coastal town in the country and during the second dive he contracted the bends.

The story goes that he was nursed by nuns but there was also talk of a girl he had met during his first trip. However, in true story book fashion, years later Robbie was away on one of his dangerous trips in some god forsaken location when he came across a softly spoken Irishman. They began to talk. Robbie is a great raconteur, especially when in his cups, and this stranger was very interested. He began to ask specific questions about various places and dates and whether or not Robbie had been there. After

212

establishing he had been in Ireland during a particular year he then asked Robbie whether he remembered a certain young lady. Robbie replied that he did but when the next question was, "Did he know that she had given birth to a son?" Robbie began to feel uneasy. The Irishman smiled and told him that all the dates fitted and that she had made a success of her business. He shook Robbie's hand and as he left said, "But of course, your red hair could never be mistaken!" In quieter moments I find myself wondering, rather wistfully, do I have a red haired grandson or not?

And so my story that began at my daughter's graveside now ends with the house.

A house that watched over the lives of my family, for better or worse, during the last nine decades. He has both enticed and entrapped, but he has touched the hearts of all the people who have lived within his walls.

And now Lucy and Tom remain trapped by their love for this old house and there are times when I wonder whether they will stay or go? Only time will tell!

Epilogue

Five months after meeting Adam I packed my bags, wrote a note and walked out on everything I had ever known, into another world!

There were many tears, as I had not realised how desperately would miss my children. However, eventually, with time, we were all together.

Adam has brought immeasurable joy into my life and I am a changed person.

One of the greatest joys was my reconciliation with my brothers and their wives. We spent holidays together, we stayed in each other's homes and we got together whenever time and distance permitted. They are all gone now, but I have such beautiful memories.

Through Adam, I was also reunited with my childhood girl friend Georgie, for which I am eternally grateful.

Adam and I have been married for twenty-six years and I pray there will be many more to come.